Logic Design

An Introduction to Digital Logic

The Maplin series

This book is part of an exciting series developed by Butterworth-Heinemann and Maplin Electronics Plc. Books in the series are practical guides which offer electronic constructors and students clear introductions to key topics. Each book is written and compiled by a leading electronics author.

Other books published in the Maplin series include:

Audio IC projects	Maplin	0 7506 2121 4
Computer interfacing	Graham Dixey	0 7506 2123 0
Music projects	R A Penfold	0 7506 2119 2
Starting Electronics	Keith Brindley	0 7506 2053 6

Logic Design

An Introduction to Digital Logic

Mike Wharton

Newnes

An imprint of Butterworth-Heinemann Ltd

Linacre House, Jordan Hill, Oxford OX2 8DP

A member of the Reed Elsevier group

OXFORD LONDON BOSTON
MUNICH NEW DELHI SINGAPORE SYDNEY
TOKYO TORONTO WELLINGTON

British Library Cataloguing in Publication Data
A catalogue record for this book is available from the
British Library
ISBN 0 7506 2122 2

Library of Congress Cataloguing in Publication Data
A catalogue record for this book is available from the
Library of Congress

 Edited by Co-publications, Loughborough

 Typeset and produced by Sylvester North, Sunderland

— all part of The Sylvester Press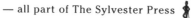

Printed in Great Britain by Clays Ltd, St Ives plc

Contents

Preface

This book is a collection of feature articles previously published as magazine articles. They were chosen for publication in book form not only because they were so popular with readers in their original magazine appearances but also because they are so relevant in the field of introductory electronics — a subject area in which it is evermore difficult to find information of a technical, knowledgeable, yet understandable nature. This book, we think is exactly that.

This is just one of the Maplin series of books published by Newnes books covering all aspects of computing and electronics. Others in the series are available from all good bookshops.

Maplin Electronics Plc also publishes a monthly electronics magazine called *Electronics*; it is the ideal choice for anyone who wants to keep up to date with the world of electronics, computing, science and technology. Practical electronics projects are included with all parts readily available.

Maplin Electronics Plc supplies a wide range of electronic components, project kits, tools, test equipment, accessories and other products to private individuals and trade customers. Telephone: (0702) 552911 or write to Maplin Electronics Plc, PO Box 3, Rayleigh, Essex SS6 8LR, for further details of product catalogue and locations of regional stores.

1 Power to the people

This first chapter outlines the design of a simple 5 volt supply for use with experiments throughout the book.

Gimme the power!

Before you can venture forth on making any project in electronics you need a supply of electrons, you need lots of them, and they must be kept moving! Common sources are cells and batteries, like the zinc-carbon and alkaline-manganese ones, but these are becoming more and more expensive, have a fairly low capacity, and are definitely non-returnable when empty! Many schools possess very rugged low-voltage power supply units (PSUs), which allow mains supply to be used with safety. These units are often able to deliver several amperes at a voltage which is variable between zero and about 20 volts. Such power supply units are fine for lighting bulbs, driving motors and copper-plating Sir's door keys during Chemistry lessons, but sensitive electronic circuits like to be supplied with more refined electrons. This chapter describes how regulated power supply units operate and how to construct one suitable for the projects in this book.

Smoothing, or, when is d.c. not d.c?

You may know that the *mains* supply in this country is described as alternating current (a.c.); this means that the current, and the voltage, is constantly changing. This is not on an irregular basis, but smoothly and regularly 50 times every second. If you think that *sounds* fast it is really quite slow compared to radio frequency (RF) voltages which may alternate at anything up to many millions of times per second. So, we have this alternating supply, and a graph of the mains voltage against time would look like Figure 1.1. Because the supply voltage alternates 50 times each second, its frequency is 50 hertz, hertz being the units used for describing frequency — named after Heinrich Hertz, but that's another story. The voltage of 230 volts marked on Figure 1.1 is the value used to describe mains voltage, i.e. 230 volts a.c. Some readers will have recognised the curve shown in Figure 1.1 as a sinewave, and that the value of 230 V is the root mean square value, or r.m.s. for short. If you didn't know

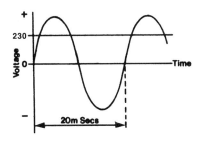

Figure 1.1   Alternating current

that don't worry, use it to impress your friends; it's actually the value of direct current (d.c.) needed to produce the same heating effect in a resistance.

You may well be wondering what all this has to do with our little d.c. power supply unit, and it's this: a.c. is great for getting the electrons from the power station into our homes, because it means that transformers can be used to step up the voltage for transmission, and then back down again. Indeed, the heart of most power supply units is a transformer which reduces the lethal 230 V mains supply voltage to a safer 20 V or so. However, a.c. is not much good for powering circuits designed to operate on d.c., because the polarity of the supply changes every half cycle, and polarity sensitive components like transistors would be zapped on the first negative wave. The simplest way to convert a.c. into a sort of d.c. is to block these negative half waves with a diode. A simple circuit, shown in Figures 1.2, will block the negative half waves, and the slightly more complicated ones in Figures 1.3 and 1.4 will produce the waveforms shown alongside.

3

Logic design

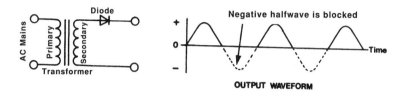

Figure 1.2　Simple diode rectifier circuit

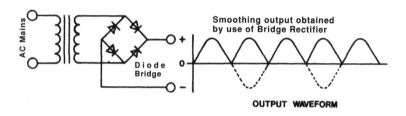

Figure 1.3　Bridge rectifier circuit

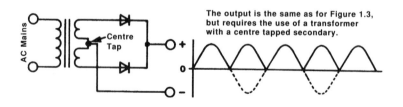

Figure 1.4　Full wave rectifier circuit

However, you couldn't really call the outputs from any of these circuits d.c., at least they're nothing like the steady voltage produced by a battery. One answer is to connect a capacitor, as shown in Figure 1.5. A capacitor connected in such a way is called a reservoir capacitor and it serves to store up electrons and let them out in a more even stream, rather like a full-size water reservoir. The resistor marked as the load in Figure 1.5 represents the circuit being supplied with current by the power supply unit; it may be just a resistor, but it's more likely to be a transistor radio, or even a whole computer, the effect is just the same. The reservoir capacitor is charged up by the current from the diode rectifiers, then, as this falls back to zero, the capacitor is able to maintain a flow of current through the load until it is charged again on the next half-cycle. The larger the load (that is, the smaller the resistance) so the more rapidly it will empty the reservoir, and hence it needs to have a fairly high value of capacitance. For small loads, taking just a few milliamps of current, then values around 1000 µF to 4700 µF will suffice, but where larger currents are involved, such as in a computer, values of 20,000 µF to 33,000 µF (20 to 33 millifarads) are needed.

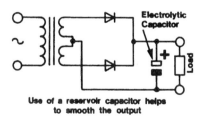

Use of a reservoir capacitor helps
to smooth the output

Figure 1.5   Use of reservoir capacitor to smoothe the output

Logic design

All this may seem sufficient to produce a fairly respectable output, but, as Figure 1.6 shows, it is still far from perfect. The output from our evolving design contains what is called *ripple* (unfortunately, not the raspberry type!). What is needed is some clever device which can compensate for the variations in the waveform, to let more current through when it falls and block it off when it rises. Although the ripple may not have a very large value, often less than half a volt, it will make its presence felt in many circuits in no uncertain manner.

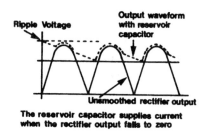

The reservoir capacitor supplies current when the rectifier output falls to zero

Figure 1.6   Ripple voltage inherent with a reservoir capacitor

Zener diode to the rescue!

Possibly the simplest way of producing a constant voltage from one which varies is to use a zener diode. The characteristics of this device are shown in Figure 1.7. In the forward biased direction it behaves like most other diodes, nothing remarkable in that; however, in the reverse direction, the current passed remains very small until a certain voltage is reached, the zener voltage, then

6

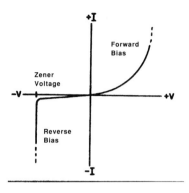

Figure 1.7 Zener diode characteristics

whoosh... a very large current will pass. To use such a device a resistance is needed in series to limit the current to a safe value, so that the diode doesn't get too hot and burn out. The zener voltage can be arranged during manufacture to be any value, and a quick look at any component catalogue shows that zener diodes are made with certain preferred values, rather like resistors. A very simple design, using a zener diode connected to the rest of the components used so far, is given in Figure 1.8. This will produce a *regulated* output, but there is a snag (there had to be a snag, life is never that easy!). Such an arrangement is only able to supply a limited current, and probably much less than any power supply unit worth the name. Ohm's law will tell you the maximum current you can draw before the output voltage falls below the zener voltage. Suppose we want a 5 volt supply to run our home computer, so we would choose a 5 V zener diode. Suppose also that having spent all the pocket money on the computer we can only afford a zener diode able to dissipate 400 milliwatts, about the cheapest available. This gives us a zener current of:

$$I = P / V$$

therefore, $I = 0.4/5$ which gives a zener current of 80 milliamps. If our unregulated supply produces 9 volts d.c., the value of the series resistor will then have to be:

$$R = V / I$$
$$\text{so,} \quad R = (9 - 5) / 0.08 \text{ ohms}$$
$$= 4 / 0.08 \text{ ohms}$$

therefore, R = 50 ohms.

So, you may well be asking, where's the snag? So far we have not taken any current by an external load; if we attach a load resistance which will pass 50 milliamps then this current will be diverted from the zener diode, so that the total current remains 80 mA, and the voltage dropped by the resistor is still 4 V. However, if we try to take more than 80 mA there will be nothing left for the zener and the voltage dropped by the resistor will be more than 4 V; in other words, zip goes our regulated

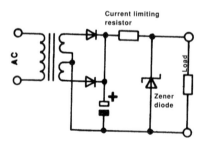

Figure 1.8   Use of a zener diode to provide a constant voltage output

supply of 5 volts, for these currents are only a small fraction of that required by even a modest computer. This type of circuit is only suitable for providing a constant voltage for critical parts of a design, such as oscillators, where it helps to maintain frequency stability, and only a small current is taken. One solution to our problem would be to use a zener diode with a larger power dissipation, but, I can hear you say, there must be a better way that doesn't turn all our expensive electrons into heat before they have a chance to do any useful work.

Head them off at the pass!

The zener diode is very good at providing a constant reference voltage, but what it really needs is more muscle. This is usually arranged by using the zener to control a power transistor, such as the 2N3055, in an arrangement known as a series pass circuit shown in Figure 1.9. Here, the original zener diode circuit is used to provide base current for the series pass transistor, which then amplifies the current available to the external load. This type of circuit is able to provide a fairly constant voltage output under varying load conditions. To go back for a moment to the example of the home computer, which may require several amperes, the transistor will drop the 4 volts, assuming the 9 volts remains the same, but pass a current which depends on the load resistance. The point to note is that although power dissipation in the zener is no longer a problem, you must take care that the limits of the power transistor are not exceeded, and this will normally be mounted on a heat sink if large currents are involved.

A practical design

All of the above theory can be put together to produce the design shown in Figure 1.10. There is nothing remarkable about the design, and many will recognise it from similar commercial designs. The capacitor connected across the zener is to ensure that the base current to the power transistor is as smooth as possible, because small variations here will be amplified and make matters worse rather than better. The appearance of a couple of extra transistors in the final design also requires some explanation. Transistor TR1 is the power transistor, which is supplied with base current from the zener diode via transistor TR2; this arrangement permits a lower zener current to be used, and transistor TR2 is needed to increase the base current to the power transistor. Transistor TR3 is included with resistor R3 to provide some degree of short circuit protection. When the voltage developed across resistor R3 due to the passage of load current increases beyond about 0.6 volts, transistor TR3 will start to conduct and divert base current away from transistor TR1 thus limiting the load current to around 2 amps. Finally, diode D5 is included to indicate that the unit is switched on.

Construction

The power supply unit may be constructed on breadboard, remembering to mount the power transistor TR1 on a suitable heat sink. A better alternative is to use a printed circuit board.

Take note — Take note — Take note — Take note

It's worth bearing in mind that because mains voltages are present at the input side of the transformer, great care must be taken to ensure that it is impossible to touch any of the *live* parts. For this reason it is a very good idea to mount the unit in a proper project box which can be earthed, otherwise you are in danger of defeating the whole object of the exercise, which is to remove the hazard of mains voltages! This should also be borne in mind if it is necessary to investigate any reasons why the unit does not function as intended; the golden rule here is make certain the mains is disconnected before probing with your fingers.

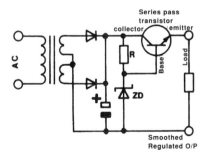

Figure 1.9   Use of a series pass transistor

Logic design

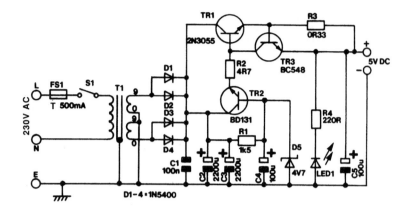

Figure 1.10   PSU circuit

A voltmeter applied to the output should indicate between 4.5 and 5.5 volts at worst, and should be close to the 5 volts required for TTL work if the unit has been put together correctly. If the voltmeter reading is outside these limits then switch off immediately and check your work; things to look out for are solder bridges across tracks on the circuit board, components incorrectly placed and the electrolytic capacitors the *wrong way round*.

Hint:

If a metal box is used, then the power transistor may be mounted on the rear of the case along with an insulating mica washer; again, remember to use wire of adequate size and rating for those connections which carry the high currents.

Power to the people

Having successfully completed the power supply unit you will then be in a position to commence the experiments on logic design without any fear of destroying the integrated circuits due to inappropriate supply voltages.

Logic design

Power supply unit parts list

Resistors — All 0.6 W 1% metal film (unless specified)

R1	1k5	1	(M1K5)
R2	4Ω7	1	(M4R7)
R3	0.33 Ω (3 W) wirewound	1	(WO.33R)
R4	220 Ω	1	(M220R)

Capacitors

C1	100 nF 50 V disc ceramic	1	(BX03D)
C2,3	2200 µF 16 V PC electrolytic	2	(FF60Q)
C4,5	100 µF 10 V PC electrolytic	2	(FF10L)

Semiconductors

D1–4	1N5400	4	(QL81C)
D5	BZY88C6V2	1	(QH09K)
LED1	Red LED	1	(WL27E)
TR1	2N3055	1	(BL45Y)
TR2	BD131	1	(QF03D)
TR3	BC548	1	(QB73Q)

Miscellaneous

T1	TR 9 V 24VA	1	(WB03D)
FS1	T 500 mA 20 mm fuse	1	(WR18U)
S1	Std toggle DPDT	1	(FH39N)
	safe 20 mm fuseholder	1	(RX96E)
	kit T03	1	(WR24B)
	wire and hardware to suit		

14

2 Chips and gates

You should by now have built, or have access to, a d.c. supply providing a regulated 5 volts. This will be used as the power supply for the various experiments which will mainly use transistor-transistor logic devices, or TTL for short. If such a supply is not available it is possible to use batteries at a pinch, although the commonly available battery voltages are either just too high or too low. For example, a 4.5 V battery may be used with no risk of damaging any chips, but as its output voltage falls with use, it may become insufficient to operate some of the devices properly. This can lead to some very misleading problems for the unwary. A 6 V dry battery, on the other hand, is really too high, although with care it can be reduced with a suitable series resistor.

Hint:

Possibly the best source in this line would be four 1.2 V Ni-Cad cells connected in series; this gives 4.8 V which will remain fairly constant during discharge. These cells may, of course, be recharged — which, of course, brings us back to a mains power supply again!

Chips with everything

A feature of modern electronic apparatus is that often somewhere lurking inside the most mundane item will be found at least one integrated circuit — commonly known as a *chip*. A glance through any electronics component catalogue will reveal that there must by now be umpteen thousands of different types, shapes and sizes of integrated circuit.

Take note — Take note — Take note — Take note

The electronic chip is distinguished from the potato variety by being packaged in a rectangular black (usually) box from which protrude two rows (usually) of sharp metal pins or legs. Its type will be indicated by a code number printed on the top side, and pin number 1 identified in one of several ways, as shown in Figure 2.1.

Chips and gates

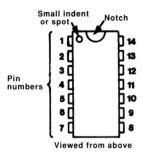

Small indent or spot   Notch

Pin numbers

Viewed from above

Figure 2.1   14-pin dual-in-line (DIL) package

All the wide variety of chips produced by modern technology may be divided into two categories, analogue and digital. We shall only be concerned at this stage with the digital variety; the analogue types (or analog, if you speak American) consist of all manner of specialist devices intended for particular applications. Further, the only digital types of integrated circuit we are concerned with in this chapter (and in the following few), of course, are those types which we've already referred to as transistor-transistor logic — TTL. There are, though, several other types of digital integrated circuits — discussed in later chapters.

Before we start any cookery with these chips it is essential that we all know and can identify the devices which are going to be needed; there are several *grades* of TTL device, and the one of interest to us is the 7400 series. Each device in this series has a specific part number, starting with the two figures 74. Thus the first in the series, 7400, is listed as a quad two-input NAND gate, which at first glance may seem to be a bit of a mouthful. What this means will be clear later, but first there are some more numbers which you will find on the package which need to be explained to avoid confusion. Figure 2.2 shows a typical chip of this type; in this case the part number is prefixed by the letters SN, which stands for *semiconductor network*, and is used by quite a few manufacturers. Other manufacturers may use other letters, such as DM, whilst some use none at all. Finally, the type number may end with a single letter, the commonest being N, which indicates a plastic package.

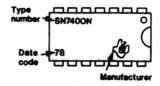

Figure 2.2 Typical markings on TTL packages

Hint:

Very often the chip will have another number stamped close to the type number, and may look similar to the type number. This is a date stamp, which indicates the week and year of manufacture. For example, the number 9533 would mean that the chip was made during week 33 of 1995; some confusion may arise if you come across old chips made during 1974, of course, so beware if you buy some *bargain packs* of suspect devices.

Take note — Take note — Take note — Take note

Several different families of TTL devices exists, and each has its own specific identification in a device's number. For example, *low power Schottky* devices only use a fraction of the current which ordinary TTL devices use. The method of identifying this type of device is to insert the letters LS after the 74 of the type number; for example, a 74LS00 would be the low power Schottky version of the standard 7400 device. Other device families (HC, HCT) also exist.

Generally, these alternative TTL families are made as pin-for-pin replacements for the standard types, and with a few exceptions may be used instead. Indeed, it is not normally usual for ordinary TTL devices to be specifically called for in any modern logic circuit design, and in some cases it is not even possible to obtain ordinary TTL devices — one of the other families' devices must be used instead.

Logic levels

As we are dealing with digital devices, it is important at the start to make certain that what this entails is properly understood. The segregation of chips into analogue and digital varieties was mentioned above, and it is true to say that one deals with analogue quantities and the other with digital quantities. An analogue quantity is one

19

which is continuously variable, and although this may be a voltage it could equally well be the amount of liquid flowing down a pipe, the speed of the wind or the intensity of light from the sun. All of these quantities can be converted into a proportional voltage by suitable means. A digital quantity, on the other hand, is one which changes by fixed amounts, with no fractional parts in between. Thus the number of people in a group is a digital amount, you cannot sensibly have three-and-two-thirds people. Likewise, in digital electronics, we are concerned with voltage signals which have just two levels, and ideally nothing in between. Using TTL devices these levels are +5 volts and 0 volts, with the +5 volt level being assigned the logic value of 1 and 0 volts a logic value of 0. There are other systems, using other voltages to represent logic levels, but we shall not concern ourselves with them.

The great advantage of the system described is that it actually makes the representation of numbers a lot easier than any analogue system; for instance, suppose you wanted to show a value of 5 using a range of voltages between 0 V and 10 V. Easy, you say, that would be given by 5 volts, but now imagine you need to show a value of 255 on the same voltage range. One solution would be to make the 10 V equal to a value of 1000, so that 255 would be given by a voltage of 2.55 volts. This would then mean that only 0.01 volt represents a value of 1, and this is such a small voltage that any practical system would be hopelessly inaccurate. By adopting a digital system any value can be created with perfect accuracy. This is the basis of the modern digital computer, but more of that later, as we are getting ahead of ourselves.

At *this* stage it is sufficient to appreciate that the presence of 5 volts, or a voltage very close to it, represents logic 1, and 0 volts, or again a value very close to that, is logic 0. These logic values do not necessarily stand for the numerical values of 1 and 0, but might equally well mean *true* and *false*, or *valid* and *invalid* in terms of logical arguments, and Figure 2.3 summarises these ideas.

VALUE	
+ 5 Volts	0 Volts
Logic 1	Logic 0
True	False
Valid	Invalid
High	Low

Figure 2.3   The positive true logic notation system

Truth tables

The introduction of the idea of logic brings us next to the subject of *truth tables*; these have been adapted from the subject of Boolean algebra as a convenient method of describing the performance of a particular logic chip. Mention of such things as Boolean algebra may have caused some of you to wonder what you might have let yourselves in for. If so, then rest assured that this book will stick to the practical path, and although it is difficult to ignore it completely, those readers wishing to delve more deeply into this fascinating subject will have to look elsewhere.

Logic design

If you have studied the subject of electronics at all before, then it is quite possible that you have come across the so-called characteristic curves for active devices such as transistors. These are used to describe in a graphical form how such things react when voltages are applied to them, and can be used to make sure that the transistor is operated under the correct conditions. Fortunately, as far as TTL chips are concerned, we can treat them as what they are — little black boxes! Although they may contain several hundred individual transistors, provided some simple rules are adhered to, it is possible to ignore this when connecting together a number of different devices. This makes it possible to make up quite complex logic designs with the ability to predict the manner in which the final circuit will behave, something which would be extremely difficult using any analogue system with separate transistors.

Figure 2.4 shows the truth table for a two input AND gate alongside the commonly used symbol for this gate in circuit diagrams. It may as well be said at this stage that although this is not a British Standard symbol, it is the one which is most likely to be found in published circuit diagrams, and there seems little point in swimming against the tide!

The explanation of the truth table given is quite straightforward; the two inputs to the logic device or *gate* are labelled A and B, while the output is C. The truth table simply summarises the various outputs which would be obtained for all possible combinations of input. Thus, if both inputs are connected to logic 0, or 0 volts, then the output will be 0 volts. Only if both inputs are connected to logic 1, or +5 volts, will an output of logic 1 be obtained. This shows why the gate is called an AND gate, since both input A AND input B must be *high* for the output to be *high*, all other combinations giving a *low* output. Figures 2.5, 2.6 and 2.7 show the corresponding truth tables and symbol for three more common logic gates; Figure 2.5 is for a two-input OR gate, Figure 2.6 a two-input NAND gate and Figure 2.7 a two-input NOR gate. The last two gates deserve a little more mention, as they are the opposites of the first two. That is, if you look at their truth tables, you will see that similar inputs produce opposite outputs, so that logically a NAND gate is a *not* AND gate and a NOR gate is a *not* OR gate.

Practical devices

In any components catalogue such as the Maplin catalogue you will see the pinouts of a number of TTL chips. You will also see that only rarely does a package contain a single device. For those without this valuable reference aid, the pinout of a 7400 is given in Figure 8. This is where we come back to that mouthful of a name used to describe such packages. Thus a 7400, which contains four identical two input NAND gates, is listed as a *quad 2-input NAND gate*, while the 7420 is a *dual 4-input NAND gate*. i.e. two NAND gates each having four inputs.

Two other pins identified in Figure 2.8 are labelled V_{cc} and GND; these are the pins to which the necessary power supply for the whole package is connected, with

Logic design

Truth Table

A	B	C
0	0	0
0	1	0
1	0	0
1	1	1

Figure 2.4   Two input AND gate

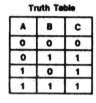

Truth Table

A	B	C
0	0	0
0	1	1
1	0	1
1	1	1

Figure 2.5   Two input OR gate

Truth Table

A	B	C
0	0	1
0	1	1
1	0	1
1	1	0

Figure 2.6   Two input NAND gate

Truth Table

A	B	C
0	0	1
0	1	0
1	0	0
1	1	0

Figure 2.7   Two input NOR gate

24

V_{cc} being connected to +5 volts and GND, or ground, to 0 volts. Usually, V_{cc} is pin 14 and GND pin 7 on a 14-pin DIL package, but there are some important exceptions, and it is wise to check the pinout when making up circuits. Bear in mind too, that if you examine published diagrams these connections are often left out for the sake of clarity, but of course the circuit will not work without them!

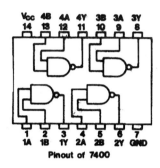

Pinout of 7400

Figure 2.8   Quad two input NAND gate

Watch your combinations

The connecting together of various logic gates, such as NAND gates and NOR gates, to produce designs with predictable output states, is called *combinational logic*. To take a very simple example to start with; suppose that the inputs of a two-input NAND gate are connected together, the truth table will become as given in Figure 2.9 as there is now effectively only one input. The result is a NOT gate, or inverter, since the output is the inverse of the input. This is also true for the NOR gate, and this is often a convenient way of producing an inverter from spare gates within a package.

Logic design

It is true to say that the NAND gate is the most versatile of all those available. as the others can be made up by a suitable combination of NAND gates. For example, Figure 2.10 shows how a two-input NOR gate may be made up by this method. You can check out the truth table for this logic array by first giving the two inputs, A and B, the value 0. Then by following the truth table for the NAND gate you can find the value of the inputs to the third gate, C and D. Continuing this process gives the input to the fourth gate, E, and finally the output F. Repeating this procedure for the other combinations of logical inputs will give the rest of the truth table.

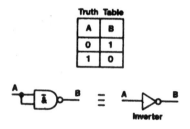

Truth Table

A	B
0	1
1	0

Inverter

Figure 2.9   NAND to NOT conversion

Figure 2.11 shows another logic array using NAND gates, but it is left to you to work out the relevant truth table. You should obtain that for an important logic gate which has not been mentioned yet, and which can be obtained in a single package, and the solution will be given in the next chapter.

26

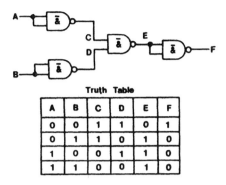

Figure 2.10   Two input NOR gate using four NAND gates

A practical solution

No doubt some of you are thinking that this is a rather theoretical approach to the problem, and would prefer a practical solution which actually involves using chips. This is the next stage in our progression along the way.

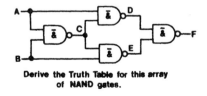

Derive the Truth Table for this array
of NAND gates.

Figure 2.11   NAND gate array

Logic design

Those who are unfamiliar with making up circuits using these types of components may welcome a few guidelines. First and foremost you will need something on which you can mount the integrated circuit package and make connections to the various pins. It is possible to solder fine wires directly to the pins, but the chips are not going to last very long this way and it is definitely not to be recommended. The most suitable method is to use a specially made *breadboard*. Several varieties are available from components catalogues such as the Maplin catalogue. These may seem rather expensive just for messing about with a couple of chips, but if you intend studying this aspect of the subject further — or indeed any other integrated circuits too — then they are a very good investment for the future.

Photo 2.1 A typical breadboard: this one is available from Maplin

As a practical exercise try making up the circuit shown in Figure 2.11; first copy out the diagram and add the pin numbers, taken from the illustration of the 7400 in Figure 2.8. Next make the connections between inputs and outputs using fine wire — solid core bell wire of 0.6 mm diameter is ideal for this. Don't forget the connections to +5 V for V_{cc} and 0 V for GND. The inputs A and B in the diagram can be connected to +5 V for logic 1, or 0 V for logic 0; if you leave them *floating*, that is not connected to either logic 1 or 0, the inputs of these devices tend to float high, i.e. assume a value of logic 1.

To find out what the logic level of the output F is for the various combinations of input there are several methods which may be used. If you possess a simple voltmeter capable of indicating around five volts or slightly more then use that, remembering that +5 V represents logic 1.

Hint:

Alternatively, a small light emitting diode (LED) is very useful, and these will be used in some later circuits. To indicate a logic 1 when lit, the LED should be connected to the output as shown in Figure 2.12; a value of 1 k is given for the resistor to limit the current taken to a safe level. The LED may seem rather dim, especially if viewed in bright light, but the temptation to reduce the value of the resistor to make the LED brighter should be avoided — you may well damage the chip. For the same reason, low voltage bulbs should not be used as these take more current than the chip can safely supply, and you may find that you have cooked your chips!

Logic design

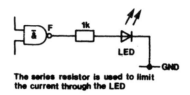

The series resistor is used to limit
the current through the LED

Figure 2.12   LED connection

3   Solution to problem

If you recall, there was a little problem left for you to
sort out in the last chapter. This was to deduce the truth
table of an array made up of two-input NAND gates, and
the result which you should have arrived at is given in
Figure 3.1. Comparison of this table with published ones
will show it to be that of the Exclusive-OR gate, (EX-OR),
also known as the Difference gate. The common symbol
for this gate, is shown in Figure 3.2(a). It is called the
Difference gate as a look at its truth table will reveal that
the output is high only when the inputs are different;
the complement of this gate is the Exclusive NOR gate,
(EX-NOR), whose symbol is shown in Figure 3.2(b). This
gate is also known as an Equivalence gate, as its output
is high when the inputs are the same, and the truth table
for this gate is shown in Figure 3.3.

Logic design

It would be possible to produce an EX-NOR gate by adding an inverter to the output of the previous EX-OR gate made up from NAND gates, thus using a total of five 2-input NAND gates. This would be quite wasteful of gates, and not surprisingly it is possible to obtain both of these devices in a single package. Thus Figure 3.4(a) shows the pinout of the 7486, a quad 2-input EX-OR gate package, and Figure 3.4(b) gives the pinout of the 74266, the EX-NOR gate package.

A	B	F
0	0	0
0	1	1
1	0	1
1	1	0

Figure 3.1   Derived truth table for 2 input exclusive OR gate

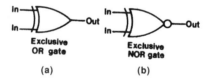

Exclusive
OR gate

Exclusive
NOR gate

(a)   (b)

Figure 3.2   Symbols

A	B	C
0	0	1
0	1	0
1	0	0
1	1	1

Figure 3.3   Truth table for exclusive NOR gate

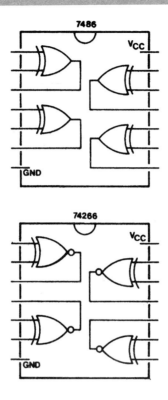

Figure 3.4   Pinouts of 7486 and 74266 chips

This now completes the list of main logic gates, although there are a few others which can be obtained, but these are really combinations of the above types in order to obtain *programmable* gates in the one package. An example of this is the 7451 AND-OR-INVERT gate, shown in Figure 3.5; here it may be seen that the package contains two AND gates connected to the input of the NOR gate. It is left as an exercise for the reader to derive the truth table for this arrangement of gates.

Logic design

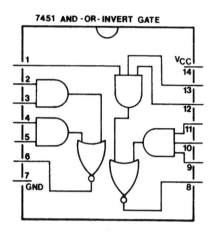

7451 AND-OR-INVERT GATE

Figure 3.5   Pinout of 7451 chip

Multi-input gates

So far we have really only concerned ourselves with gates having one or two inputs. Many of the devices available have more than this, as a glance at a component catalogue will reveal. For example, the 7430 is an 8-input NAND gate, shown for reference in Figure 3.6 along with its truth table. Fortunately, this does not make the understanding of these gates that much more difficult. If you look back at the previous truth tables, as well as the one for the 8-input NAND gate, you will see that they all have a unique output state. Exceptions to this rule are the truth tables for the EX-OR and EX-NOR gates — which are special cases. The other gates have just one value of logic output for a particular set of inputs; for example, in a 2-input AND gate the output is always low except

34

when both inputs are high. In a 2-input NAND gate, the output is always high, except when both inputs are high, and this follows on for the 8-input NAND gate, where the output is always high except when all the inputs are high.

That this is so can be tested by connecting up a 7430 on a breadboard with a LED wired to the output, as shown in the last chapter. If each of the inputs is connected to logic 1 then the output will be found to be at logic 0, with the LED extinguished. If one of the inputs is now taken to logic 0, then the LED will light up, and will remain alight while any number of inputs are held at logic 0.

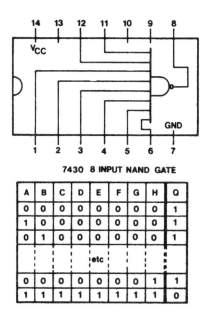

Figure 3.6   Pinout and truth table of 7430 chip

Logic design

The use of such a device may be demonstrated by referring to the part of a circuit shown in Figure 3.7. The problem here was to produce a signal from the output of the 8-input NAND gate after the counter had counted a selectable number of clock pulses. To achieve this action, each of the inputs is connected to logic 1 by a *pull-up* resistor, thereby ensuring that the output will be logic 0. The numbers shown by the outputs from the BCD counter are the number of clock pulses which need to be counted before that particular output goes high, assuming a start from zero. Without going into any further detail of how the outputs from the counter would appear, by connecting the appropriate links it is possible to set the circuit to count any value of pulses from 1 to 255. For example, if it were required to count up to 23 clock pulses before a logic 0 appeared at the output of the NAND gate, then the links for 1, 2, 4 and 16 would be made, as 1+2+4+16=23.

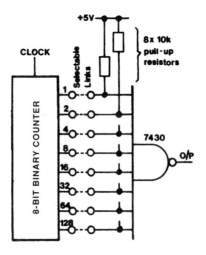

Figure 3.7 Part of counter/decoder circuit

Solution to problem

The individual pull-up resistors are needed on the inputs in order to ensure that any unconnected inputs are held at logic 1; the value of these resistors is not all that critical, but it must be remembered that the output of the counter will be required to sink the current through them when it goes low. The BCD counter is a rather different type of animal from the ones we have encountered so far, belonging to the breed of sequential logic devices. This is a whole range of beasties which will be dealt with in a lot more detail in a later chapter.

Arithmetic logic units

Any reader who has perused books or articles on the subject of microprocessors or microcomputers, and these days it's hard to avoid them, may well have come across the term *arithmetic logic unit*, or ALU. This is the part of the microprocessor which is concerned with *doing sums* and other logical operations. Needless to say, in a real life processor, this section contains a multitude of functional devices, but it is possible to emulate one of its basic building blocks, the *adder*. Side-stepping the old jokes about venomous snakes, the digital adder comes in two types, the half-adder and the full-adder. However, before we delve into the workings of these circuits, it may well be a good idea to brush up on some binary arithmetic.

I am sure everyone reading this is fully conversant with denary arithmetic, that is working in powers of ten. In binary arithmetic the same rules apply, but in this case

Logic design

we are using the number base of two, with the digits 0 and 1. When two denary (or decimal) digits are added together there are two possible situations:

●   a third digit, larger than the other two results, but smaller than the base of the number system, e.g.,

$$
\begin{array}{c}
5 \\
+3 \\
\hline
8
\end{array}
\qquad\qquad
\begin{array}{c}
1 \\
+4 \\
\hline
5
\end{array}
$$

The new digit, 8 or 5 in these examples, is called the *sum*.

●   the third digit is equal to or larger than the base of the number system, e.g.,

	5		8
	+6		+7
1	1	1	5
carry	sum	carry	sum

In this case the position of the digits comes into play and the answer consists of two parts, the *sum* and the *carry*. The generation of *sum* and *carry* occurs whatever number base is in use. In binary addition the generation of *carry* bits occurs much more often, as there are only two digits.

	0		0		1
	+0		+1		+1
	0		1	1	0
	sum		sum	carry	sum

38

These examples cover nearly all possible combinations of binary addition, the only other one being where the 0 and 1 are reversed in the middle example!

Where binary numbers containing more than one digit are to be added, then the process can be broken down into a series of repeated two-digit additions, until the process is complete. For example:

$$
\begin{array}{r}
10 \\
+01 \\
\hline
11
\end{array}
\qquad\qquad
\begin{array}{r}
111 \\
+010 \\
\hline
1001
\end{array}
$$

In the second example, the addition of the first (righthand) digits of 0 and 1 gives a *sum* of 1, and no *carry*; adding the next two digits, 1 and 1, produces a *sum* of 0 and a *carry* of 1. The next stage is to add together 0, 1 and the *carry*; as before 0 and 1 give a *partial sum* of 1, and adding the 1 carried over gives a *sum* of 0 and a *carry* into the next column. The simple rules of binary addition may be summarised in a truth table, shown in Figure 3.8.

A	B	SUM	CARRY
0	0	0	0
0	1	1	0
1	0	1	0
1	1	0	1

Figure 3.8 Binary addition truth table

39

Logic design

Looking at this table it is possible to see that a *sum* OR a *carry* is the result of a binary addition, never a *sum* AND a *carry*. To perform this operation with logic gates, it is only necessary to find ones which have the same truth table as that for binary addition. The circuit would require two inputs, A and B and two outputs to correspond to the *sum* and *carry*. This can, in fact, be achieved in several different ways; if you look back at the truth table for the EX-OR gate and the AND gate it is apparent that the *sum* part is the same as the EX-OR truth table and the *carry* part is the same as the AND gate. Actually, this is not quite a full solution, as no account has been taken of the fact that a *carry* bit may have been produced by an earlier stage, and hence this is known as the half-adder.

Half-adder circuit

A digital half-adder circuit may be made up, on a breadboard, following the diagram given in Figure 3.9. Here it can be seen that the two gates which are required are the EX-OR and the AND gates. Possibly the most convenient method of making up this circuit is to use single gates from a 7486 and a 7408, and connect them up as shown. In this case the two bits to be added are applied to inputs A and B to give the *sum* and *carry* appear at the corresponding outputs. It is also possible, remember, to make up such gates as these from the common NAND gate. We have already seen how the EX-OR gate may be made up from four 2-input NAND gates, and so to complete the picture Figure 3.10 shows how the AND gate

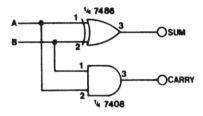

Figure 3.9 Circuit for half adder

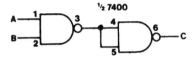

Figure 3.10 AND gate using NAND gates

may be fashioned. It is left as a further exercise for the reader to make up the half-adder circuit from NAND gates and confirm that it is logically identical to the first design.

Full-adder design

The half-adder is incomplete in that no provision is made for a *carry-in* from a previous stage. In the case of the full-adder, not only is account taken of this, but also a provision is made for the possible generation of a *carry-out* to subsequent stages. Again, the requirements of the

41

Logic design

full-adder may best be summarised in the form of a truth table; this will need to have three inputs, A,B and *carry-in*, with two outputs, *sum* and *carry-out*, as shown in Figure 3.11. The full-adder is, in essence, two half-adders connected together to take account of the extra bit carried in. The circuit for the full-adder is given in Figure 3.12. Again, although this is shown made up from discrete gates, it can also be done with NAND gates in the same manner as the half-adder.

A	B	CARRY IN	SUM	CARRY OUT
0	0	0	0	0
0	0	1	1	0
0	1	0	1	0
0	1	1	0	1
1	0	0	1	0
1	0	1	0	1
1	1	0	0	1
1	1	1	1	1

Figure 3.11   Truth table for binary full-adder

Hint:

If more than two bits are to be summed then the block can be repeated, with the carry-out from one stage being connected to the carry-in of the next stage.

42

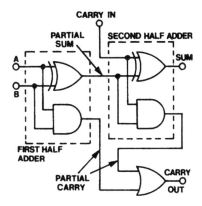

Figure 3.12 Full-adder design

Finally, Figure 3.13 shows a couple of full-adders being used to add binary 11 and 11, giving 110; i.e. decimal 3 + 3 = 6.

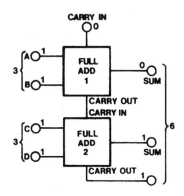

Figure 3.13 Full-adders cascaded

43

Logic design

Address decoding

Still on the microprocessor scene, another important use of TTL combinational logic designs is in the area of address decoding. The essential problem here is to produce a signal in response to a unique pattern of bits on the microprocessor address bus. This pattern of bits is, of course, the address of the device which is being sought in order to send or receive data along the data bus of the system. Typically, there may be 16 address lines, each of which is set to either 1 or 0 according to the specific address which the microprocessor wishes to access. The address is set in response to the requirements of the controlling program or software, and the logic must ensure that only one device is enabled if data bus contention is not to arise. With 16 address lines there are 65,536 possible unique addresses, corresponding to the locations in the memory map of the system. There are a number of logic devices which have been specially devised for address decoding, but we will consider a smaller problem using devices already described.

In some systems, the lower eight address lines are used by the microprocessor for a special purpose, that of addressing input or output devices which allow information to be fed between the processor and the *outside world*. With only eight lines the number of possible addresses is reduced to 256, which helps to bring the problem down to more manageable proportions. What is needed, then, is a logical *black box* into which may be sent the eight address lines along with signals to set a certain address, and from which emerges one line carrying the logic signal to select the particular device being addressed.

Solution to problem

One solution to this problem is given in Figure 3.14 and again this may be breadboarded to see how it works. One input of the EX-OR gates is connected to the address bus, and the other used to select the address of the device. The output of each EX-OR gate is then NANDed, so that the final output goes low when the appropriate address appears on the address bus. This low signal could be connected to the *chip select*, (CS) pin of the chosen device or combined with other control bus signals for further decoding. Suppose the address of the input/output device corresponds to the following bit pattern:

Most significant bit ↔ least significant bit

(MSB) 11010011 (LSB)

If this pattern is set on the inputs to the EX-OR gates then all the outputs from them will go high when the two bit patterns coincide. This in turn will set the inputs to the 8-input NAND gate all high, which is the only condition for the output to go low.

The required address may be fixed in a practical application by *hard-wiring* the selecting inputs to the desired pattern; alternatively, the inputs may be connected via DIP switches, so that the address may be changed by altering the position of the switches.

A more convenient way of describing a bit pattern, such as the one in the above example, is to use the hexadecimal system. We shall be looking at this in more detail in the next chapter for any readers who are not familiar with the system. It will also be useful when dealing with

Logic design

the other main group of TTL devices — those concerned with *sequential logic*, which we shall start to have a look at in the next chapter.

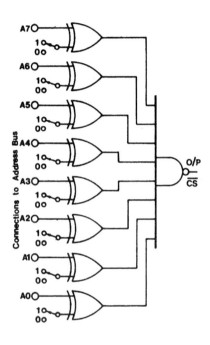

Figure 3.14   A solution to the problem of selecting a particular device from eight parallel address lines

4 Hexadecimal numbers

As promised in the last chapter, we shall commence this time with a short refresher on hexadecimal numbers — *hex* for short. We are all fairly familiar with the denary, or decimal, system, where the number base is ten. We had a brief encounter in the last chapter with the binary system, where the number base is two. In the hex system the number base is sixteen. There are some very good reasons for using such a system, rather than the more usual decimal one, which we shall go into in a moment. One potential *problem* with this method of numbering is that the same symbols as those for the decimal system are used, plus the first six letters of the alphabet. So as to be sure which number system is intended, it is usual to include some form of specifier along with the hex number, in order clearly to distinguish it

Logic design

from a decimal value. Figure 4.1 shows the relation between decimal and hex numbers. If we take decimal 42 as an example, this converts to 2A in hex, i.e. (2 x 16 = 32) + (A x 1 = 10). So 32 + 10 = 42. This would typically be written as 2AH, £2A or &2A, where the H, $£$ and $&$ symbols are used to indicate that the value is in hex. This will be familiar territory to those readers who are interested in computing, and it is recommended that anyone wanting to delve further into the theory of related number systems look up the subject in any of the books on computing. Again, some of you may be forgiven for thinking that we are wandering away from the subject of digital logic design! In fact the hex system springs more naturally from the binary way of numbering, which is the basis of practically all digital counting techniques. Before we examine some practical devices, let us just look at how digital signals are used in counting; Figure 4.2(a) shows the simplest situation, where one *line* can be used to signify two values, that is either a binary 0 or 1. Figure 4.2(b) shows how the range of binary numbers can be increased by the use of two lines; each line can adopt either of the two binary states and hence may be used to indicate values from 0 to decimal 3. The addition of one more line to the system doubles the range of values which

Dec	Hex	Dec	Hex	Dec	Hex	Dec	Hex
0	0	4	4	8	8	12	C
1	1	5	5	9	9	13	D
2	2	6	6	10	A	14	E
3	3	7	7	11	B	15	F

Figure 4.1   Decimal to hex conversion table

(a)   A = Logic 1 (+5V)
      or A = Logic 0 (0V)

(b) A = 0 or 1
    B = 0 or 1

A	B	Value
0	0	0
0	1	1
1	0	2
1	1	3

(c)

A	B	C	D	Value
0	0	0	0	0
0	0	0	1	1
0	0	1	0	2
0	0	1	1	3
0	1	0	0	4
0	1	0	1	5
0	1	1	0	6
0	1	1	1	7
1	0	0	0	8
1	0	0	1	9
1	0	1	0	10
1	0	1	1	11
1	1	0	0	12
1	1	0	1	13
1	1	1	0	14
1	1	1	1	15

Figure 4.2 Digital counting

can be shown, thus with four lines it is possible to indicate up to decimal 15, as in Figure 4.2(c). This is where the convenience of counting in a base of sixteen comes into its own. Thus, with a group of four connecting wires or *bus*, the sixteen values from 0 to 15, or 00 to 0F hex can be produced. In many home computers a bus consisting of 8 lines is used, allowing the 256 values from 0 to 255, or 00 to FF hex to be transmitted as data.

Logic design

Clocks

When numbers are to be used for counting we generally need something to count. Some *digital* counting methods use fingers, but we will try for a little more sophistication! In sequential logic designs, the logic levels change as pulses are fed through the system. These pulses are produced by special oscillators, often called clock oscillators or, simply, clocks. The connection with the clock on the wall is that the duration of these clock pulses sets the speed of operation of the circuitry; the faster the clock then the quicker the circuit operates. In the analogue world, an oscillator will usually be required to produce the smooth curve of a sinewave. In digital circuits such waveforms would be an embarrassment, as they are slowly changing voltage levels present between the positive and negative peaks. What is required is a waveform which shows rapid transitions between logic 0 and logic 1; this is found in the square wave, shown in Figure 4.3. Ideally the transitions, known as the rise time and fall time, should be as rapid as possible. A good square wave oscillator may produce rise and fall times of a few nanoseconds, although for general experimentation times much longer will do.

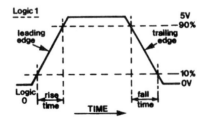

Figure 4.3   Square wave

Simple clock oscillator

The simplest clock for use in logic designs could be just a push switch, connected as shown in Figure 4.4. The main drawbacks with such a simple method are two-fold:

● contact bounce when the switch is opened and closed will give rapid, multiple pulses, rather than the single pulse intended and,

● your finger will soon get tired if a continuous stream of pulses is needed!

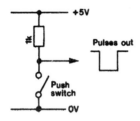

Figure 4.4   Simple switch pulser

Nevertheless, it is a very useful way of *single-stepping* pulses through a circuit if bounce is eliminated. A method of doing this using a single chip is shown in Figure 4.5, but again this may not be necessary for simple experiments. A clock oscillator providing a series of square pulses can conveniently be made using the common 555 timer chip. There must have been umpteen designs published showing how this device may be used in the so-called astable mode. Figure 4.6 shows one such 555-based clock oscillator which will give an output of around 60 Hz.

51

Logic design

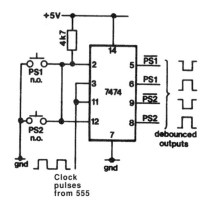

Figure 4.5 Debounced push switch

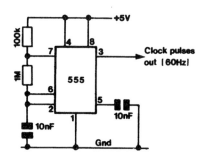

Figure 4.6 555 clock oscillator

Counting pulses

Having devised a method of producing pulses, the next step will be to look at digital methods of counting them. Of course, if you are producing pulses by pushing a switch you can count them as you go along, but this is

52

not really the name of the game. Figure 4.7 shows the pinout of a 7493 four bit binary counter chip. The drawing gives little clue as to what is going on inside the device, but at this stage this is not important. What is important is that we understand how to connect it up correctly. One point to notice immediately is that the connections to +5 volts and ground are on different pins from many 74 type chips — pins 5 and 10 respectively. The 7493 has four counting stages altogether, with the output from the first stage being available separately. The outputs and inputs of the last three stages are connected together internally. The train of pulses from a push switch or clock oscillator is fed into pin 14, input A. The first stage divides the pulse rate by two and the output appears at pin 12, Qa. For the remaining stages to be brought into the chain, this output is fed back into input B at pin 1. The outputs from the subsequent stages then appear at pins 9, 8 and 11, that is, Qb, Qc and Qd. The final two pins which deserve special mention are pins 2 and 3, labelled R1 and R2. These are *reset* inputs and if not connected will float high and force the outputs Qa to Qd to remain fixed at logic 0. For the chip to be enabled

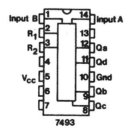

Figure 4.7 Pinout of the 7493

Logic design

both these pins must be connected to logic 0. Finally, the logic levels at the outputs can be displayed by connecting an LED to each one, via a 1 k current limiting resistor as explained before. An illuminated LED indicates a logic 1 at that output and an unlit one a logic 0. Figure 4.8 shows the circuit for the 7493 to operate as a four bit binary counter, using a simple push switch to produce a series of pulses. If the counting sequence starts from 0000 (all LEDs out), then it should be possible to verify that the sequence of outputs follows the pattern given earlier in Figure 4.2(c). Thus this circuit can be used to count a series of up to 16 pulses before returning to zero again. If a larger range is required then two 7493s can be used, with the Qd output of the first one being connected to the input A of the second one. This would then give eight data line outputs, providing a counting range of 0 to 255 decimal, or 00 to FF hex as mentioned at the beginning of this chapter. Next chapter we shall delve more deeply into counters, and bring together a number of the aspects of digital design into a simple timer project.

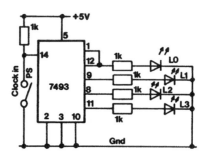

Figure 4.8   7493 four bit binary counter

54

5 Building a timer/counter

We have almost come to the stage where some of the topics covered in previous chapters can be brought together in a simple project. This will not be a *state of the art* design and hence not offered as a complete kit of parts. What is intended is to illustrate how a timer/counter circuit may be made up using several functional integrated circuits, rather than a single VLSI device. In fact, it would make an ideal candidate for construction on a breadboard, as outlined in an earlier chapter.

Loose ends

First there are a couple of loose ends which ought to be tied up before we go much further, and the first of these

Logic design

concerns the nature of TTL output stages. As a general rule, one should never connect the outputs from any logic gates together. Indeed, it is one of the common mistakes in wiring up a breadboard circuit which should be particularly looked for. If it is not corrected then this is a very good way of zapping the chip when the power is applied. The reason for this is because of the type of output configuration used in TTL output stages, which is shown diagramatically in Figure 5.1. The use of a complementary pair of transistors like this is often called a *totem pole* output. The effect is to ensure that the voltage swings as close to +5 V or 0 V (logic 1 or 0) as possible, depending on the state required by the logic. A TTL output is described as being able to sink or source a certain amount of current, for the following reason. In order for the logic level of the output of Figure 5.1 to be 1, then transistor A will be *on* and transistor B will be *off*. Thus current can flow through transistor A from the 5 V supply to the load and thence to ground. Alternatively, if the logic level of the output is at 0, then transistor A will be *off* and transistor B will now be *on*. In this case current can flow into the output stage from a load which has one end connected to the +5 V supply. In the first instance the output stage is acting as a current source and in the second instance it is a current sink. Both of these arrangements are shown in Figures 5.2(a) and 5.2(b); the LED will light when the logic output is 1 for the first case, and when the logic output is 0 in the second case. In both instances a current limiting resistor is shown, as otherwise the current through one of the output transistors would be more than it could tolerate, and it would be destroyed, rendering the whole of the logic gate useless.

56

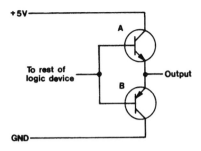

Figure 5.1   Simplified TTL output stage

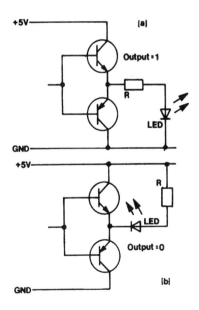

Figure 5.2   Current source and current sink

Logic design

The same thing will happen if two outputs are connected together, as indicated in Figure 5.3. Everything is fine so long as both outputs remain at either logic 0 or 1, as then the voltage at the output will be the same and no current will flow.

However, as soon as the outputs are different, then current can flow through one transistor in each output stage, with one acting as a source and the other as a sink. The current will be limited only by the *on* state resistance of each transistor and sooner, rather than later, one or both will burn out. It is a practical result of Murphy's law which will ensure that the devices are ruined before you can spot the mistake and turn off the power!

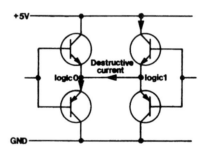

Figure 5.3   Outputs connected together

Open collector outputs

Connection of logic gate output stages together is possible if gates with *open collector outputs* are used. The arrangement in such an output stage is shown in Figure 5.4. Here, the output must be connected to an external collector load, usually a resistance of around 1 k. In this case, the output voltage will be pulled up to logic 1 by this resistor when the output transistor is *off*. When the transistor is turned *on* the output will go to logic 0 as current flows through the collector load resistor. A number of separate output stages may share a common load resistor without any danger of damage as they can only act as current sinks. If one output is *off* and another is *on*, no current flows through the *off* transistor; likewise, if several transistors are *on* then the current through the load resistance will be more or less shared by each one. This type of output connection is also sometimes called *wired-OR*, since the arrangement is similar to the use of diodes and a resistor to form a simple OR gate.

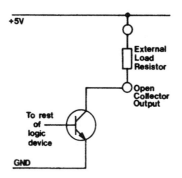

Figure 5.4   Open collector output stage

59

Logic design

Synchronous and asynchronous counters

The second *loose end* which needs paying attention to relates to another feature of the output stages of TTL dividers or counters. So far we have considered one particular device, the 7493, or its low-power Schottky counterpart, the 74LS93. If you look up either of these two devices in a component catalogue you will see them described as 4-bit binary ripple counters, and this needs a little explanation. Firstly, the reference to 4-bits relates to the number of individual bits available at the output; in this case with four bits the maximum binary value which may be obtained is 1111, or 15 decimal. In some cases this can be a bit of a nuisance (pun not intended!) where decimal values are required, but more on that in due course. More important is the reference to them being ripple counters. This means that the outputs do not change state exactly together, and the use of the word *ripple* indicates something of the internal working of these devices.

If you refer to the diagram of such devices you may recall that the output from the first stage was fed back to the input to the second and subsequent stages. In operation, as clock pulses are fed into the chain of counting circuits, the output from the first stage acts as the clock for the second stage, the output of the second stage then clocks the third stage, and so on. It can be imagined that each clock pulse passes along the chain of divider stages like a wave, and as the wave passes the outputs change, one after the other. Such a device is then described as being *asynchronous*, as the outputs do not change in step. This can often be a great inconvenience, especially

60

when the outputs are to be connected into a logic array designed to respond to a certain set of output states. The unexpected states appearing at the inputs to such a decoder would produce *glitches* which would almost certainly prevent the correct operation of the rest of the circuitry.

In order to get round problems such as these, it is necessary to employ a device whose outputs do all change in step, that is a *synchronous* counter or divider. Here, the outputs will change state exactly in step, either on the leading or trailing edge of the input clock pulse. Since there are no *illegal* states present at the outputs, they may be used to trigger other events within the circuit without any fear of problems due to glitches. A TTL 4-bit synchronous counter is the 74161 or 74LS161; this is slightly more difficult to make than the asynchronous 7493 device, and the opportunity is taken by the manufacturer to incorporate other features within this package.

Decoders and displays

The main object of this chapter is to examine the rest of the circuitry needed to make up a simple counter/timer. We shall also graduate from the use of simple LEDs to indicate binary values to 7-segment LED displays for showing decimal numbers.

This then brings us on to the topic of another range of devices called: decoders. These are used to convert the binary output from a counter to the correct pattern for operating a 7-segment display. As is often the case, there are a variety of devices available for this purpose, but we shall consider only one. Most decoders intended for use with 7-segment displays have output stages which are able to deliver the required current to drive such displays directly, that is without a separate buffer chip. In this case these devices are more correctly termed decoder/drivers. The pinout of a typical decoder/driver, the 7448, is shown in Figure 5.5; here the inputs are on the left and the outputs are on the right. The inputs may be connected directly to the outputs of the counter, such as the 7493, and the outputs to the 7-segment display.

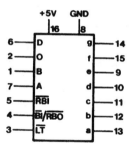

Figure 5.5   7448 BCD to 7-segment decoder/driver chip

A decoder of this sort may be regarded as a simple *read only memory*, (or ROM, of which more in a later chapter). The truth table of this device is, of course, fixed and is shown in Figure 5.6. For each of the 16 possible combinations of the inputs A, B, C and D, the internal logic will set the outputs to that for the corresponding decimal number. The outputs are marked a, b, c, d, e, f and g, and these match the segments of the display, as shown in Figure 5.7.

Dec NO	D	C	B	A	a	b	c	d	e	f	g
0	0	0	0	0	1	1	1	1	1	1	0
1	0	0	0	1	0	1	1	0	0	0	0
2	0	0	1	0	1	1	0	1	1	0	1
3	0	0	1	1	1	1	1	1	0	0	1
4	0	1	0	0	0	1	1	0	0	1	1
5	0	1	0	1	1	0	1	1	0	1	1
6	0	1	1	0	1	0	1	1	1	1	1
7	0	1	1	1	1	1	1	0	0	0	0
8	1	0	0	0	1	1	1	1	1	1	1
9	1	0	0	1	1	1	1	1	0	1	1

Figure 5.6   Truth table for 7448

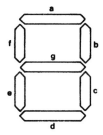

Figure 5.7   Segment identification

In order to reduce the number of connections to the display, either the cathodes or the anodes of the individual LEDs are connected together. In the first instance the display is referred to as a *common cathode display* and in the second as a *common anode display*. Of course, in order to obtain sensible digits, the appropriate type must be used with a particular driver.

63

Logic design

The 7448 has outputs which are *high* for the corresponding binary input; this means that an LED display must be used which has all the cathodes connected together and to ground. A suitable version from Maplin is, BY68Y which is a double digit type.

The chosen device, the 7448 (or 74LS48) has the open collector type of output described earlier. The method of connection to the LED display is thus shown in Figure 5.8; the output from the driver stage is connected directly to the corresponding segment, and each segment has its own pull-up resistor to +5 V. The value of resistance will need to be chosen such that the current is limited to around 10 mA for each segment. With a 5 volt TTL supply and red LEDs having a forward voltage drop, V_f, of 1.6 V, the resistance is found from:

$$\frac{(5 - 1.6)}{10} = 340 \text{ ohms}$$

A preferred value of 330 or even 470 ohms will be satisfactory.

The circuit may be made up as shown in Figure 5.8, but there are a few remaining details which need to be explained. Looking at the pinout of the 7448 reveals some pins which have not yet been mentioned, i.e. those marked LT, BI/RBO and RBI, each of which has an overbar indicating that it is an active low input. The first, LT, stands for lamp test, and when taken to a logic 0 will cause all the segments to be lit, irrespective of the data inputs. In this application it must be connected to logic 1, +5 V. The other two inputs are the blanking input/ripple blanking output and the ripple blanking input. These are used when several 7448s are used in cascade in or-

64

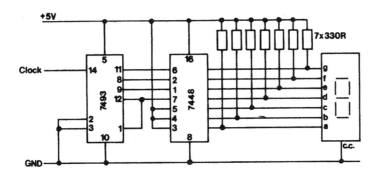

Figure 5.8   TTL counter with 7-segment display output

der to blank out leading or trailing zeros in a multi-digit display, which helps to conserve power. In this application these inputs should be connected to logic 1, otherwise the display will be blanked out! However, once the circuit has been made up, don't hesitate to experiment and try to ascertain the effect of different logic levels on these pins. This would be more interesting if, say, two or three digits were used, but more of this in a later chapter.

The input for the 7493 counter may be obtained from any of the clock sources outlined in the previous chapter. If a simple push switch is used, then the display will show the decimal number of *pushes*; however if a 555 timer is used and the component values are chosen to give a period of 1 second, then the display will show elapsed time in seconds. It is not easy to obtain an accurate timebase of one second from such a simple circuit, and for greater accuracy it is usual to employ a crystal-controlled oscillator. A typical frequency of crystal-controlled oscillator is 32,768 hertz, and a chain of dividers is used to reduce this down to a frequency of 1 hertz, or a period of one second. The number of divide-by-two stages needed would be 15, and although this could be achieved using four 7493s, it would be a very inefficient and cumbersome arrangement. Needless to say, there are devices which can do all this, and more, in a single device.

Finally, the divider referred to throughout this chapter has been the 7493, which is a 4-bit device. This means that it is able to count up to 15 decimal, while the 7448 is only a *binary coded decimal*, or bcd, device. There will be six outputs, from 10 to 15, which cannot be represented on a single digit, and the 7448 will give a blank display for these inputs. A rather more suitable device for this application is the 7490 (or 74LS90) which is a decade counter. This will count up to decimal 9 and then go to 0 on the next clock pulse. It is pin-compatible with the 7493, and may be used as a direct replacement in the above circuits. The only thing which needs to be done is to take account of pins 6 and 7, labelled R9(1) and R9(2). These may be used to reset the counter outputs to 1001, i.e. decimal 9, rather than zero. In the above application both pins will need to be connected to logic 0, in order for the counter to operate.

In the next chapter we shall examine the subject of drivers and displays further and start to look at shift registers of various types.

6 More chips

The first chapter in this book explained something of the meaning of the various numbers to be found on a *chip* package. So far we have dealt almost exclusively with TTL devices and described the use of the two main types. These are the standard 74 type devices and the 74LS range, that is the low power Schottky ones. So far no mention has been made of any of that other vast family of devices, the CMOS integrated circuits, and this will be remedied later.

During the last few years there have been great advances in the technology involved in the manufacture of integrated circuits and this in turn has led to the production of other types of device. Many of these are made as pin-compatible versions of the original 74 variety, but with

Logic design

some particular feature. Table 6.1 gives a list of the types of devices available along with a brief summary of their characteristic features. The last of these, the 74HC and 74HCT series are really a development of the CMOS types mentioned above, but the continued improvements have been such that the previously clear-cut distinction between TTL and CMOS types has been eroded.

Pros and cons

Perhaps this would be a suitable point at which to mention further some of the reasons why two ranges of devices have been developed in the first place. The standard TTL devices were the first on the scene, and arose

74	Original *standard* TTL range.
74L/74H	Obsolete ranges offering lower power consumption or higher speed respectively.
74S	High speed devices using Schottky diode techniques, but increased power consumption.
74LS	Improved version featuring both low power consumption and increased speed.
74ALS/74F	Advanced low-power Schottky (or Fairchild *Fast*) featuring improved speed and power consumption.
74C	CMOS versions of standard TTL devices, but with many devices in the TTL range not available.
74HC	High speed CMOS devices; one of the latest ranges offering most of the best features of both CMOS and TTL devices i.e. low power and highspeed.
74HCT	A development of the 74HC devices, but where the input logic levels have been tailored to match the standard TTL range.

Table 6.1 Summary of available TTL types

68

out of the development of bipolar transistors, on which they are based. This was quite some time before MOS (*metal oxide semiconductor*) devices had been invented. Although TTL got off to a head start, it soon became apparent that this technique had a natural limitation to the number of individual transistors that could be packed on to the silicon chip. This mainly revolved around the amount of power dissipated by each tiny transistor, and the associated problem of removing the heat generated as a consequence. If the transistors were packed too closely on the surface of the chip then the temperature would rise to levels that easily destroyed the delicate structures. On the other hand, MOS transistors consume very little power and hence can be packed more closely together without creating the problem of an intolerable temperature rise. Needless to say, the fabrication of MOS-based integrated circuits was not without other problems, for instance, their susceptibility to static discharges, which was not shared by the TTL types.

The ability to pack more MOS and later CMOS (*complementary metal oxide semiconductor*) devices led to the production of more complicated devices; that is with even larger scales of integration. Thus although TTL are generally limited to small and medium scales of integration (SSI and MSI), the CMOS devices and their offspring are able to be produced with large, very large and now ultra large scales of integration (LSI, VLSI and ULSI). It is this sort of advance which, of course, has led in turn to the advent of the microprocessor chip, and all that it has brought in its wake.

The upshot of all this is that both sets of devices have some real advantages over the other:

Logic design

- TTL devices tend to be much faster than CMOS,

- CMOS devices consume much less power than TTL,

- TTL devices are not likely to be destroyed by static,

- CMOS devices are available with higher scales of integration.

As mentioned before we shall be diverting our attention to the CMOS devices in future chapters.

Three-state outputs

Before moving on to the main topic, it is appropriate to explain about one more type of logic output arrangement. In the last chapter, mention was made of the decidedly ill-effects which can be caused if standard TTL outputs are connected together. One way round this which was described, is to use what are called open-collector outputs. In many computer or microprocessor based systems it is often necessary for devices to share a common line in order to form what is called a *bus*. Although it is perfectly possible to do this using devices with open collector outputs, this method is now somewhat old-fashioned, and has been superseded by a much better one. Many devices are now produced which are specifically designed with outputs suitable for connection to a common bus. These are commonly called *three-state* outputs, as the output may be at a logic 0, a logic 1, or a third state which is neither 0 nor 1, but a high impedance state. Forcing the output to this third state is effectively equivalent to disconnecting the device from the bus. This makes the interconnection of many devices sharing a common bus a much easier task, and only requires the inclusion of an extra control signal to select those devices who may have access to the bus without causing any problems over bus contention. Thus at any one time only two devices will be connected together, a sender and a receiver, (or a *talker* and a *listener*) while all the rest are 3-stated. Other descriptions of devices with this type of output which may be encountered are tri-state (which is actually a trade mark of National Semiconductor), TSL, three-state logic and three-state TTL.

The extra control pin required by such devices is usually labelled *enable/disable*, *output enable* or *chip select*, and permits the logic device to behave normally, or else disconnects the output of the device from the rest of the circuit. One group in particular which make use of this feature are memory devices, and it is to these we now turn our attention.

Memory

The idea of an electronic component which can store *data* is not of recent origin, but its implementation in a physically small device was yet another step along the road to the implementation of the modern digital computer. It must be admitted at the outset though, that most of these devices are based on MOS technology and are not really suitable for breadboard experimentation. There are, however, a number of standard TTL devices which are eminently suitable for such an application. One reason why they are useful is that their memory capacity is limited, just the reason why they are not to be found in a microcomputer!

The particular chip we shall look at— the 7489 — is actually not readily available (although you might be able to find one if you shop around). Nevertheless, it *does* give a good introduction to memory.

Static RAM

The 7489 is described as a 64-bit static RAM, and this needs a little explanation. Firstly, remember that we are dealing with digital devices and that the *data* will be stored as *bi*nary digi*ts* or *bits*. The significance of any stored data can be what we want it to be; it may be just numbers stored in their binary form, or it could be that the numbers represent the letters of the alphabet, or whatever. This device then, can hold just 64-bits, each either a 0 or a 1. The *static* part of the description is not an indication that it will stand still while you look at it! Rather it serves to put it into one family of memory devices, the other most common type being described as *dynamic*. This second type of memory works in a rather different manner to the static variety and continually needs to be *refreshed*, otherwise it would forget what data it contained. The two types of device store bits in different ways. The static variety, for example, store bits by setting or resetting little bistable flip-flops. The dynamic type is based on CMOS technology, and store their bits as an electric charge on a tiny capacitor. Since the charge which can be held is so small and tends to leak away, it has to be *topped up* every so often to maintain the data intact. Typically, the time between successive refreshes will be about 1 millisecond, and in a microprocessor based system this will be carried out automatically, and is one reason why they are unsuitable for breadboard experiments.

Take note — Take note — Take note — Take note

The RAM part of the description, as some readers may well know, stands for *random access memory*. This puts it into a particular family of memory devices, the other main family being the ROMs or *read only memories*. These two descriptions are a little misleading, especially in the case of RAM. Essentially what it means is that any location within the devices can be accessed with equal ease, rather than them each having to be accessed in sequence until the desired location is reached.

Functional groups

So much for a general description of semiconductor memory, now for a look at the 7489 in particular. Figures 6.l(a) and 6.1(b) show two pinouts of this device. Figure 6.l(a) is the usual one, showing the function of the various pins. Figure 6.1(b) is simply a rearrangement of the pins into their respective groups. Here again, some explanation will be in order for the beginner.

Logic design

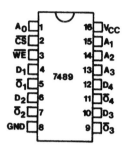

Figure 6.1(a)   Pinout of 7489, 64-bit static RAM

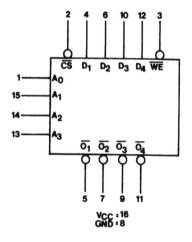

Figure 6.1(b)   Logic diagram of 7489

The arrangement of pins on the package is arrived at for the convenience of the manufacturer, and Figure 1(b) shows a logic diagram which is more helpful when drawing up complicated circuit designs, rather than slavishly following the pinout and ending up with a *rats nest* of interconnecting lines. The groups of connections associated with any memory device are:

74

● address lines — there are four of these on the 7489, shown on the diagram as A0 to A3,

● data lines — these are shown as D1 to D4 and also $\overline{O1}$ to $\overline{O4}$. In the case of the 7489, data being fed into the device enters along the input lines D1 to D4, whilst data leaves along output lines $\overline{O1}$ to $\overline{O4}$. The over-bar on this last set indicating that the data leaving any location is the inverse of that which was fed in. Thus a 0 will be output as a 1, and vice versa,

● control lines — the 7489 has two control lines, labelled as $\overline{CS}$ and $\overline{WE}$; here again the over-bar indicating that they are both active low and need to be taken to logic 0 to have the required action. CS stands for *chip select* and WE for *write enable*,

● power lines — power needs to be supplied to the chip, which in this case is just +5 V to V_{cc} and 0 V to GND; many other memory devices often require several other voltages.

Memory circuit

If you've been lucky enough to find a 7489, the design of the circuit to put the chip through its paces is shown in Figure 6.2. This is slightly complicated and requires careful assembly on a breadboard. One tip for anyone wishing to assemble this circuit is to make a copy, (a photocopy if you're that lucky) and to check off each connection on the diagram as it is made. Also it pays to be neat and methodical, by making connections to each pin of a device in order, starting at pin 1 and working round the

Logic design

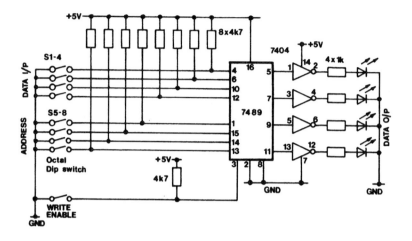

Figure 6.2   Circuit for investigating the 7489

pins in turn. Neatness alone is no particular virtue, but it makes life a little easier if your circuit doesn't work perfectly first time; if the only way to sort out a rat's nest of wires is to dismantle it and start again you might just as well have taken the time to do it right in the first place!

The purpose of this circuit is quite straightforward; that is, to fill each location or *address* in the 7489 with a binary number or *data*. This is achieved by setting the address lines to a particular binary value, then setting the data lines in a similar fashion, and finally writing the data into the address by pulsing the *write enable* pin low momentarily. The address and data line logic levels could be set up using wires which are swapped over between logic 1 and 0 in order to produce the desired combination, but at this stage it would be a lot more convenient if DIP switches were used. A total of eight switches are needed, four for addresses and four for data, and an octal version would be suitable.

The data output from the device is inverted, and the purpose of the four gates from the 7404 is to invert it back to its true form. The outputs of the 7404 are then connected to the four LEDs in order to display the value of the binary data at any particular address; as usual, a logic 1 is represented by a lit LED. Although not shown on the circuit diagram, four more LEDs could be connected across the address lines in order to display the value of the address selected on the DIP switches, but this is by no means essential.

The sequence of writing to a memory location is to set the DIP switches to the required value, say all at logic 0 for the first address. As the switches are changed, with the power turned on of course, the output LEDs may change, indicating the contents of any other addresses selected. After first switching on it is very likely that the addresses will contain random numbers or all logic ls or 0s. Having set the address then set the required data using the other four DIP switches. This data is then written into the chosen address by taking the write enable pin to logic 0. This can be done simply by moving a wander lead from logic 1 to logic 0, or by using a push switch as shown in the diagram; it is immaterial whether it is debounced. On pulsing the $\overline{WE}$ pin low like this, the LEDs indicating the data output should change to the same value as that set on the data input switches. With the $\overline{WE}$ pin back at logic 1 the next address and data value can be set up, and then written into memory by pulsing $\overline{WE}$ low. This procedure may then be repeated for the whole of the 16 possible addresses.

Logic design

In order to inspect the contents of a particular address it is only necessary to set up the appropriate value on the DIP switches, when the output LEDs will display the data contained at that address. If the power is disconnected, even for a fraction of a second, then all the data stored will be lost and replaced by random *garbage*. For this reason such memory devices are also known as *volatile*, since if power is removed the stored data effectively *evaporates*!

Organisation of memory

This arrangement of setting data and addresses by the use of switches is rather tedious, but it does demonstrate the basic steps involved with nearly all memory devices in filling them with information. Of course in this device which has four address lines there are only 16 possible unique locations at which to store data. Each location is arranged to hold four bits of data, hence 16 x 4 = 64 bits in total. An important aspect of any device is how the memory is organised; in this instance it is as sixteen 4-bit words. A typical device which might be found in a microcomputer is the 2114 static RAM. This is described as a 4 K memory chip, and this means that it can hold a total of 4096 bits, since in computer parlance 1 K (not 1 k) is not 1000 but 1024, being 2 raised to the power of ten. These 4096 bits are organised as 1024 4-bit words. Another common device found in similar applications is the 4116 dynamic RAM. This one is described us a 16 K device, and in this case the memory is organised as 16384 x l-bit words (16 x 1024 = 16384). For this device to be

More chips

used in practical designs, where useful word lengths are
needed, it is necessary to connect them in parallel. For
example, if an 8-bit word is required then eight 4116s
are used, giving a total amount of memory of 16 kilobytes,
usually written as 16 K, as eight bits equal 1 byte. In fact
a byte can be any length, but if other than eight it is usually first stated in the manner: *4-bit byte* or *16-bit byte*
for example.

Sequential addressing

The method of setting the address and data lines with
switches can be improved upon by the use of a device
which was used in the last chapter. This is the 7493 counter, and Figure 6.3 shows how two such devices can be
used to replace the eight DIP switches of the previous
circuit with just two push switches. With this design it
is possible to obtain the required values of address and
data by sequencing the 7493s in turn then pulsing the
$\overline{\text{WE}}$ pin low, as before. This makes entry of the sixteen
values much quicker and easier, even though the full
range of addresses has to be sequenced through until a
particular one is obtained.

The final circuit, shown in Figure 6.4, is a combination of
this design and the one from the last chapter. To refresh
your memory, this was using a 7493 to produce a 4-bit
binary sequence to drive a 7448 7-segment decoder/
driver. The 7493 produces a fixed sequence of binary
outputs, being the binary equivalent of the numbers 0 to
15. In Figure 4 the 7489 memory chip has been inserted

Logic design

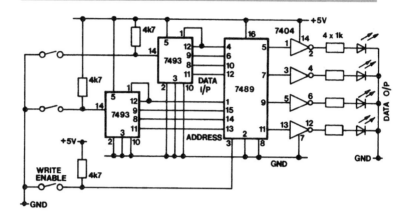

Figure 6.3 Use of a 7493 to sequence the address and data lines

between the output of the 7493 counter and the input to the 7448 decoder/driver. Now, by sequencing through the addresses to the 7489 it is possible to enter any value of 4-bit word, and this will then be produced as the input to the 7448. Thus, it is easily arranged to alter the fixed sequence of numbers on the 7-segment LED to any that is desired. For example, by storing the binary equivalents of 15 down to 0, the display will count down as the addresses are sequenced, rather than count up. Alternatively, data may be stored which produces a random counting sequence, or one which replaces the six illegal inputs for the 7448, i.e. those which produce either a blank or a meaningless display, with a repeat of other numbers.

80

Hint:

This last circuit will require a fair amount of time and patience to wire up on a breadboard, and if it doesn't work properly first time then you will have to supply the necessary logic (pun intended) to sort out the errors! This again requires a methodical approach, trying to narrow down the area containing the mistake(s). Avoid the temptation to change connections at random or without any plan of action; the first thing to check is if you have made the correct connections to V_{cc} and ground to each chip before you set about wholesale dismantling of the circuit. Hopefully you will meet with success and have gained invaluable first-hand experience in the use of these devices, and be well prepared to tackle those contained in the next chapter.

Logic design

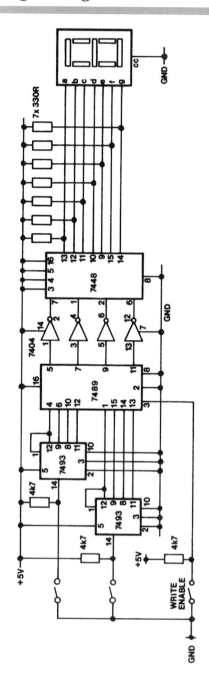

Figure 6.4 Circuit for using the 7489 with a 7448 7-segment decoder/driver

82

7 CMOS devices

As mentioned in the last chapter, there is available a range of logic devices based on a different type of technology from that of TTL devices. TTL chips have resulted from developments in bipolar transistors, that is the common-or-garden type like the ubiquitous BC109 and its ilk. The term bipolar is used to describe the manner in which the electrical current is carried through the transistor, which is by two charge carriers called electrons and *holes*. The electron we are all familiar with, in a manner of speaking, being the basic particle carrying a unit negative charge; a *hole*, on the other hand, is simply the absence of an electron within the crystal structure of the semi-conductor material. It is really beyond the scope of this book to delve further into the theory of semiconductor action, but suffice to say that this type of device has certain electrical features which have been used to advantage in TTL devices.

Logic design

Many readers will be quite aware that besides bipolar transistors there are the so-called FETs or *field effect transistors*. In these devices the charge is carried only by electrons, there being no involvement with *holes*. FETs have been developed along different lines to give several families, from *junction gate FETs*, (JUGFETs) to *insulated gate FETs*, (IGFETs). A widely used member of this last family is the MOSFET, or *metal oxide semiconductor FET*, and it is distantly related cousins of these that form the basis of the *complementary metal oxide semiconductor*, or CMOS, logic devices. Figure 7.1 shows how CMOS transistors are fabricated on the surface of a silicon chip, while Figures 7.2(a) and 7.2(b) give an indication of the internal circuitry of typical CMOS and TTL devices.

As mentioned earlier, there are a variety of advantages and disadvantages associated with both kinds of device, but it seems that many of the disadvantages with the CMOS variety are rapidly being overcome and they are poised to become the major type of logic element. Briefly, their most serious problem has been the low speed of operation as compared with TTL devices, but this may be off-set by their much reduced power consumption and wider operating voltage. For CMOS devices the supply positive is connected to V_{dd} (drain voltage), and supply negative to V_{ss} (source voltage). The negative is connected to source since it can be regarded as the *source* of negatively charged electrons. Practically all CMOS devices will tolerate a range of supply voltages from 3 to 15 volts, and hence may be operated quite happily from a standard TTL supply of 5 volts.

Many of the logic elements available in TTL have direct equivalents in CMOS, indeed, some are even pin-

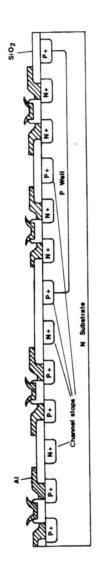

Figure 7.1 Conventional metal gate CMOS structure

Logic design

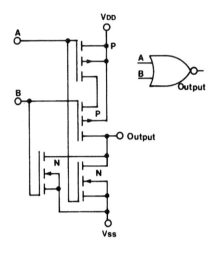

Figure 7.2(a)   CMOS 2-input NOR gate

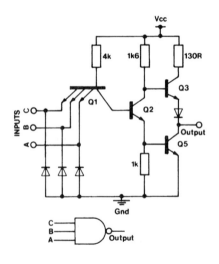

Figure 7.2(b)   TTL 3-input NAND gate

86

compatible replacements. A glance through a component catalogue will give a very good idea of the range of devices commonly available along with their respective pinouts. Pretty well all of the circuits given so far in this book can be implemented using CMOS devices, and Figure 7.3 shows one of the earlier ideas but using a CMOS chip, the 4520. Because of the larger scales of integration possible with CMOS, this actually contains two four-bit binary counters within the 16-pin package, and the internal arrangement is a little different from the 7493 which was used in the original design.

Beware of static!

This point is perhaps a convenient one at which to mention one of the problems of using CMOS devices which is never encountered with TTL, that of sensitivity to static discharges. One may inadvertently destroy a CMOS device by careless handling even before it is put into the circuit. The reason for this is due to the nature of the input to this type of device; the layer of insulating silicon dioxide, shown in Figure 7.1, is extremely thin, typically only a few microns thick. It is very easy to generate high static charges due to friction; for example by walking across a synthetic fibre carpet in rubber-soled shoes it is possible to produce a charge of 10,000 volts. Normally this would quickly leak away, but if applied to a CMOS chip then the thin oxide layer may break down and the device is effectively destroyed. Most of the devices produced nowadays have some form of protection against static discharge, usually in the form of internal zener diodes. However, the protection is not completely effective, and some care needs to be taken.

Logic design

The usual advice is to work on an earthed metal tray with all manner of other anti-static precautions, but for the common logic devices this is not really necessary. Provided you avoid touching the pins when handling them and resist the temptation to polish them up on your woolly jumper, no *dead* chips should be produced.

Also, it is a good idea to store them in their anti-static tubes or with the pins pushed into polystyrene foam which has been covered with aluminium cooking foil, so that the pins are all effectively shorted together.

Take note — Take note — Take note — Take note

One word of caution, don't adopt too much of a cavalier attitude to them or you might be tempted to treat a microprocessor in the same way, with expensive results!

CMOS logic gates

One very useful effect of the insulated gate construction of these devices and its associated high input resistance is that some *tricks* are feasible which would be difficult or impossible with TTL gates. For example, Figure 7.4 shows how a simple squarewave oscillator, or astable flip-flop, may be obtained from just two gates. The frequency of operation is set by the values of capacitor and

88

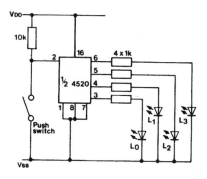

Figure 7.3   4520 dual 4-bit binary counter

resistor chosen, but the exact frequency will be determined to some extent by the gate input characteristics, which will vary slightly from device to device. The approximate frequency of operation is found from the empirical formula:

$$f = 0.6/C \times R$$

where frequency, f, is in Hertz, capacitance is in Farads and resistance is in ohms and with an upper frequency set by the natural limitations of these devices. Similarly, Figure 7.5 shows a monostable flip-flop made up from two gates; due to the high input resistance long time constants can be achieved by the use of relatively small value capacitors in conjunction with large resistors. The period of this type of monostable is given by another form of the above expression:

$$t = 0.6 \times C \times R$$

where C and R are as before and t is the period in seconds.

89

Logic design

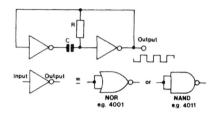

Figure 7.4   CMOS astable formed by two inverters

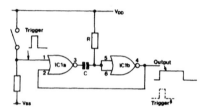

Figure 7.5   Monostable formed by two 2-input NOR gates

A third type of flip-flop is shown in Figure 7.6. This is the bistable flip-flop, which is so called because it can adopt either of two stable states, and a suitable trigger pulse can flip it from one state to the other, where it remains until it is triggered to flop back.

CMOS counters

Some of the above ideas are brought together in Figure 7.7. You should now have some idea as to the function of the circuit, which is a simple timer to count up to 59

90

CMOS devices

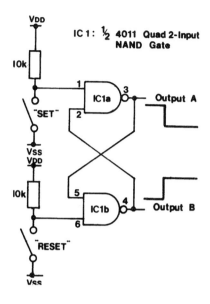

Figure 7.6   Bistable formed by two 2-input NAND gates

seconds and then reset to 00. The clock pulses are obtained from an astable flip-flop which has a period of
about one second. Because of the simple nature of this
part of the design the overall accuracy of the timer will
not be very good; a much more accurate method of gen-
erating clock pulses is discussed later. The clock pulses
are fed into one half of a 4518 binary coded decimal (BCD)
counter. The outputs from this counter are then used to
operate a 4511 BCD to seven segment decoder/driver for
the *units* LED display. The output from the most significant bit (MSB) of the first half of the 4518 is then used as
the clock input to the second half of the counter, which

91

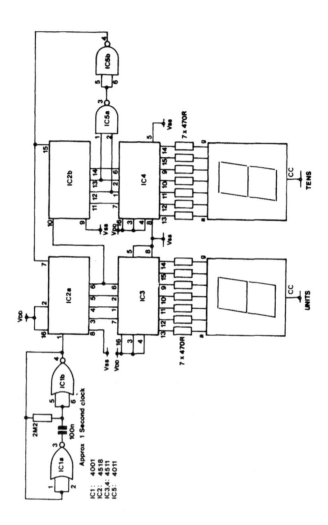

Figure 7.7 Simple seconds timer

produces the required output for the *tens*, via the second 4511 and LED display. The extra gating of IC5(a) and IC5(b) is to detect the presence of the value 6 on the output from the second counter, as it is desired only to count up to 59 and then reset to zero. The method of achieving this is to connect both the 4 and the 2 output lines to the inputs of a two-input AND gate, as the value of 6 is present when 4 and 2 are both at logic 1. You may well be wondering, then, why two NAND gates are shown in the diagram. This is simply to avoid purchasing a chip containing AND gates when the job can be done with the more versatile NAND gates. The two NAND gates connected as shown, of course, produce an AND gate, as reference to previous truth tables reveals.

The output from the AND gate is then fed to the reset pins on both counters, so that counting is forced to recommence from zero. Actually, a figure 6 will appear on the display, but only for the time it takes for the reset signal to be gated through the decoder and counter, which is of the order of a few nanoseconds, so you are unlikely to see it! Of course, it is possible to detect other values, so that instead of counting minutes some other number is counted. Without any reset logic, i.e. with the reset pins connected permanently to ground (or V_{ss}), the circuit will count up to 99 before cycling round to zero again. The reader is left to experiment, the only requirement being to AND all the unique values of the next highest count together to the reset pins. For example, if it were desired to display the value 60, then 61 would need to be detected by ANDing 4 and 2 from the tens counter, along with 1 from the units counter. This could be achieved with a three-input AND gate or more conveniently with an equivalent array composed of two-input

NAND gates. This kind of decoding can be done with this counter since it is of the synchronous type, described in the last chapter.

Jeepers bleepers!

Returning to the simple oscillators made up from a couple of CMOS gates, and incorporating some of the ideas outlined above, brings us to the final portion of this chapter's logic feast.

Although the output stages of CMOS gates are unable to drive even a small loudspeaker directly, they are ideal for operating the small piezo-electric sounders for producing an audible note. Such sounders require some care in soldering on a couple of connecting wires, but they have the advantage of being cheap. Figure 7.8 shows a circuit which has an output of around 1 kHz, which may be used to test the transducer. The audio output can be increased by the use of an extra gate, as indicated in Figure 7.9, but even then it will not be rock-crushing! By employing another set of gates operating at a much lower frequency it is possible to control the audio oscillator to produce a pulsating tone, as shown in Figure 7.10. Developing this idea further, it is then possible to control this circuit with yet another one, this time a monostable with a period of, say, 5 seconds. When initiated, the circuit of Figure 7.11 will produce a pulsed tone for this duration, and could be used as an audible warning device. Finally, Figure 7.12 shows how this last idea can be added to the simple timer outlined above, so that a warning note is sounded when a particular time is reached on the counters, in this case at every minute mark.

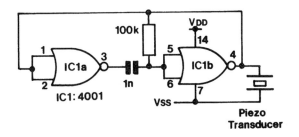

Figure 7.8   Astable used to operate a piezo-electric sounder

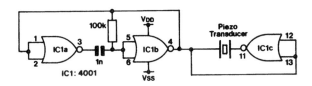

Figure 7.9   Circuit for increased output

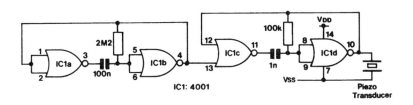

Figure 7.10   Gated astable to produce pulsating tone

Logic design

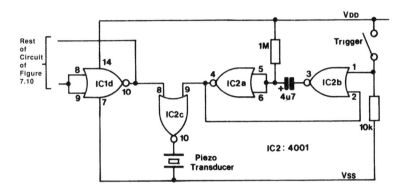

Figure 7.11   Monostable used to gate pulsed astable

If you have a requirement for a simple timer of this nature, then the design could well be made up into a more permanent form, rather than being left as a breadboard experiment. In such a case it would be better if the features of the design were more versatile; for example, if the *alarm time* could be set to any value over a wider range of times, to produce a high technology egg-timer! You may have some idea as to how this might be achieved, but the next chapter will include a suitable design, as well as probing deeper into the use of other interesting CMOS devices.

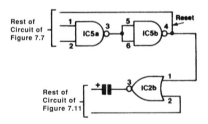

Figure 7.12   Reset pulse used to trigger monostable for audible warning device

8 Crystals

In the last chapter, mention was made of a method for improving the accuracy of an oscillator to be used for timing purposes. The most common method of regulating the frequency of an oscillator is to make it crystal-controlled, as many of you will be aware. The material generally used for this purpose is quartz, a naturally occurring mineral which exhibits the piezo-electric effect. This means that if a voltage is applied to the prepared faces of a crystal of quartz then it changes its shape very slightly. Conversely, if a crystal is distorted slightly by the application of pressure, then a voltage is generated across the same faces. By carefully cutting the crystal of quartz to an accurate size and shape it is possible to ensure that it resonates at a particular frequency, rather like a tiny bell. If such a device is placed in the feedback path of an oscillator circuit, then maximum feedback will occur at the resonant frequency of the crystal and the vibration of the crystal, and hence the oscillation of the circuit, will be maintained. Quartz is chosen as it is cheap, exhibits a fairly marked piezoelectric effect and can be made to have a very low dependence on temperature. For highly critical applications the crystal may be contained in an oven, where the temperature is thermostatically controlled. For most everyday applications this is not necessary, and the accuracy of the modern digital watch is as much a tribute to the crystallographer's art as it is to the silicon sculptors.

Reference to Figure 8.1 will give some idea of what the crystal looks like when fitted with its hermetically sealed tin can overcoat, and any component catalogue will give some more information about commonly available types. One point that is perhaps worth mentioning here is that of the 3rd and 5th overtone types. Like a violin string a crystal will vibrate at its lowest or fundamental frequency, as shown in Figure 8.2(a). However, both string and crystal can be made to vibrate at higher frequencies, and the third harmonic mode is illustrated in Figure 8.2(b). A 3rd overtone crystal has been specially cut so that it will vibrate in this manner, at a frequency three times higher than its fundamental. It is a matter of physics that the size of the crystal must reduce for an increase in resonant frequency, and to obtain the higher frequencies with the fundamental mode would mean trying to cut impossibly small crystals. A circuit for using overtone crystals will therefore contain inductive elements in order to operate at a nominal high frequency, and the presence of the crystal will ensure this is accurately maintained.

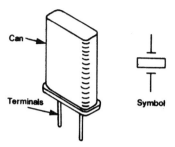

Figure 8.1   Quartz crystal

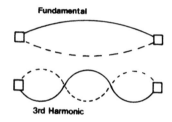

Figure 8.2(a) and (b)   Fundamental and third hormonic types

Crystal clock

Figure 8.3 shows a typical arrangement for using a quartz crystal with logic gates to produce a clock oscillator. Of course, discrete transistors could well be used in any manner of oscillator circuit, but it is often more convenient to use available gates in existing devices within a design. Here the logic devices are being used in a so-called *linear* mode, that is as amplifying elements, with the crystal fixing the frequency of oscillation. In this

99

Logic design

application the frequency will be the fundamental of whatever crystal is used, be it an overtone type or not. This kind of circuit will be found in many designs where an accurate clock is required, from expensive microcomputer controlled machines to our humble hi-tech egg-timer!

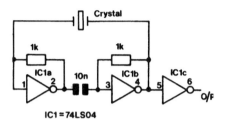

Figure 8.3   Crystal oscillator using TTL logic gates

While for many applications the use of a crystal provides an accurate timebase, it may also replace one problem with another. For instance, if we desire to count seconds in a simple timer it is impossible to provide a crystal controlled clock oscillator with a frequency of one hertz. Usually the basic frequency will be at least some tens of kilohertz and this will need to be divided down to give the desired clock rate. In a digital watch a small crystal is used which has a fundamental frequency of 32.768 kHz, and this is passed through a sequence of 16 dividers to produce a 1 hertz clock. For some mains powered equipment a 50 Hz back-up clock needs to be provided in order to keep some vital processes going until the power is restored. In this case a 3.2768 MHz crystal would be used instead.

100

Crystals

To produce a clock by using discrete logic elements for the oscillator followed by up to 22 division stages would require a lot of unnecessarily expensive chips. The whole operation can be achieved by the use of special chips, which contain an oscillator and many dividers in one package. One example of such a device in CMOS logic is the 4060, and Figure 8.4 shows how this may be used by the addition of a suitable crystal and the various frequencies tapped off from the outputs from the divider chain. Such a clock could be used to replace the simple 555 timer circuit used previously for a 1 Hz clock timer. This probably represents an over-kill for this application, but if a crystal is available it is instructive to set up the circuit on a breadboard, especially if an oscilloscope is available to examine the outputs from the dividers.

Egg timer

At the end of the last chapter it was suggested that you think about how the simple timer unit given could be improved to make it more versatile. There are almost limitless ways in which this could be achieved, and rather than giving a single complete method we shall continue by examining various options in outline. Hopefully this will give sufficient insight into the techniques to allow you to devise your own digital egg-timer.

One fairly important requirement for a timer is that it should be possible to set it to indicate a certain lapsed time. For practical reasons we shall limit ourselves to periods of less than 10 minutes, but the techniques can

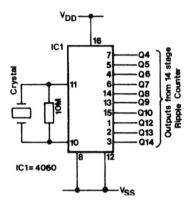

Figure 8.4   CMOS 4060 clock

be taken as far as you wish. The solution adopted may be to set the desired time and then count down until zero is reached, or to start from zero and count up until the lapsed time is detected. In each case some form of *memory* will be required. This may hold the initial value of time, which is then decremented, or to hold a time value with which each incremented value is compared until a match is found. This *memory* could be a semiconductor type or switches set to the desired time value. Besides this a clock will be needed and possibly a display to indicate how far timing has progressed.

Let us now examine how each of these solutions may be put into effect. Figure 8.5(a) and 8.5(b) are block diagrams of each one. In the first example most of the requirements have been dealt with previously, but one which has not is the method of setting the time value in some sort of memory. This could be done with some RAM

102

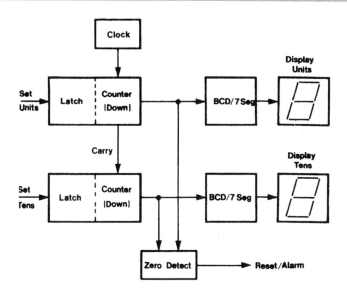

Figure 8.5(a)   Down counter

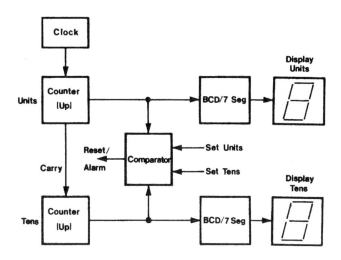

Figure 8.5(b)   Up counter

Logic design

and associated circuitry, but is more economically achieved by using *presettable up/down counters*. These are a special type which can be set to hold some desired value before being clocked down to zero; the arrival at zero may then be used to initiate a reset or alarm. Figure 8.6 gives a design using two 74LS192 presettable BCD up/down counters. This has one set of inputs, D0 to D3 and one set of outputs Q0 to Q3. When pin 11, PL (*parallel load*), is pulsed low the value present on the inputs D0 to D3 is latched into the internal dividers, then appears at the outputs Q0 to Q3. The device has two separate clock inputs, CPu and CPd. The clock pulses are applied to CPd in order to decrement the value to zero. To permit the cascading of such counters two further pins provide a *carry out*, TCu when counting up and TCd for counting down. Pin 14, MR, provides the usual *reset to zero* facility. The values for loading into the counters are shown being presented by simple switches, such as a bank of eight DIP switches. With a little ingenuity you would see that these could well be replaced by a couple of ordinary BCD counters clocked by another oscillator, or from a higher frequency in a divider chain. These would be operated by just two push switches to set the values, but as they would also need some sort of display, or share a single display, this represents an unnecessary escalation of complexity for demonstration purposes.

As given, the design will count up to 99 seconds, and longer times can be achieved by adding another stage; under these circumstances it is easier to keep the counting in seconds, say up to 999 seconds, (16 mins. 39 secs.), rather than again adding the complication of counting minutes and seconds. The arrival at zero of the outputs

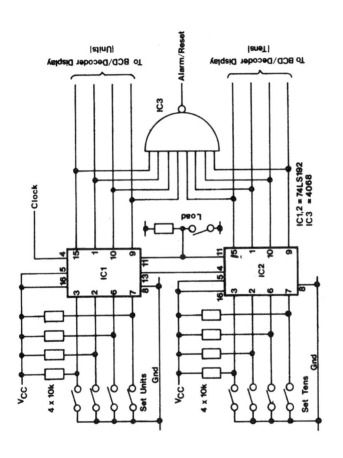

Figure 8.6 Design using up/down counters

105

Logic design

from each counter can then be detected by applying them to an eight input NAND gate. When each input has attained a logic low state the output will go high, and may be used to reset the counters, inhibit the clock or initiate an alarm circuit.

The second option is shown in Figure 8.7. This is somewhat similar to the first, but here the time value is held by a pair of special BCD encoded thumbwheel edge switches. Reference to a component catalogue will give a good idea of what these look like for those unfamiliar with them. As before, the same effect can be obtained with ordinary switches, but the advantage of this type is that it displays the value set and it is more convenient for connection directly to logic gates. For this approach a simple BCD counter such as the TTL 7490 may be used, as here, or the two contained in the single 4518 CMOS package. The other main requirement is for some form of *comparator* to produce an output when the value set by the thumbwheel switches and the counters is the same. Again, there are several ways of achieving the same end, from the use of special comparator chips to an implementation in combinational logic. The method shown in the design uses a pair of open collector Exclusive OR gate packages, an idea taken from one of the earlier chapters.

In each of these approaches the BCD decoders and 7-segment displays could be dispensed with altogether, and reliance placed on the value displayed on the edge switches. Alternatively, additional 7-segment displays might be added, one set to indicate the set time and the original to show the lapsed time.

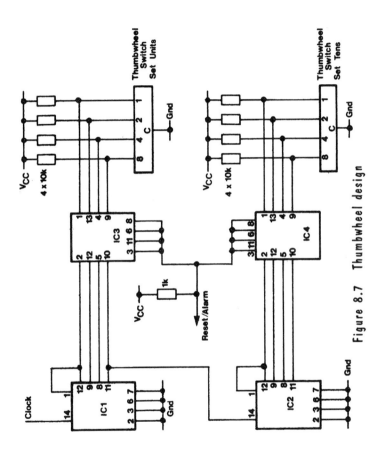

Figure 8.7 Thumbwheel design

Logic design

So much for counters and timers, and it is left to you to think of further variations on this theme. Next chapter we shall be examining the ideas behind multiplexing as well as making a start on the mysteries of the chips associated with microprocessors.

9 Multiplexing

In systems where data has to be sent from one device to another, it would appear to be convenient if each signal had its own line, and which only contained the same signal. This apparent convenience disappears where many signal lines are required, because the multiplicity of wires and separate connections would tend to overwhelm the rest of the circuitry. Moreover, there is another consideration where integrated circuits are involved, as the major portion of the cost of these is due to the cost of packaging. Thus, there is an economic incentive to reduce the pin count (i.e. the number of legs) on an integrated circuit to a minimum.

The idea of multiplexing is thus simply one of allowing different signals to share a common line or interconnection. Obviously, it would be meaningless if all possible

Logic design

signals had access to the line at the same time, and some arrangement for sharing has to be laid down. For digital signals this is usually done on a time basis, each signal having access for a fixed time in turn; this is known as *time division multiplexing*.

Let us now look at a simple example of what is involved in this idea. As before it is a circuit which may be made up on a breadboard and tested practically. Figure 9.1 shows the circuit diagram which contains both a multiplexer and a demultiplexer; the 74150 is the multiplexer and the 74154 the demultiplexer. A train of clock pulses forms the input data to the 74150 at channel 8 and leaves at channel 3 on the 74154. How are the channels selected? On the 74150 the 4-bit binary word 1000 is applied to the channel select pins, D C B A. On the 74154 the 4-bit word 0011 is applied to the output channel select pins. It is thus possible to select any one of 16 input channels and any one of 16 output channels using the two sets of 4-bit binary inputs.

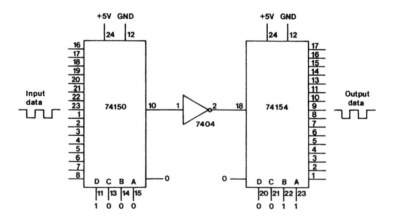

Figure 9.1   Circuit containing a multiplexer and a demultiplexer

110

One possible use of this type of combination is to minimise the number of wires needed over which to send TTL data. In this case, it is more convenient to connect the channel select lines together, as shown in Figure 9.2. Instead of a possible 16 lines, the data may be transmitted by just 6; 4 for the channel select, 1 for data and 1 for common return. The channel select lines would probably be connected to a 7490 or 7493 binary counter, and sequence through the channels 0–16. The only disadvantage is that the data on each channel is not transmitted simultaneously.

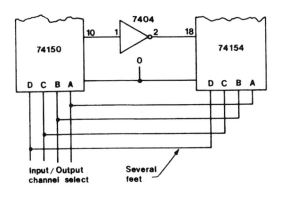

Figure 9.2   Channel select lines connected

A second example of a slightly different nature is shown in Figure 9.3. This employs a 7442 BCD to decimal decoder as a 1-of-8 demultiplexer. Figure 9.4 shows the truth table of the 7442; notice that the output lines 8 and 9 are not used, for these cannot be selected with only a 3-bit binary word. Clearly, the 7442 may be used to

Logic design

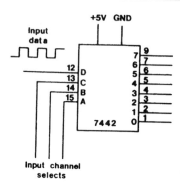

Figure 9.3   Using a 7442

Truth table for 7442

INPUTS				OUTPUTS							
D	C	B	A	0	1	2	3	4	5	6	7
0	0	0	0	0	1	1	1	1	1	1	1
0	0	0	1	1	0	1	1	1	1	1	1
0	0	1	0	1	1	0	1	1	1	1	1
0	0	1	1	1	1	1	0	1	1	1	1
0	1	0	0	1	1	1	1	0	1	1	1
0	1	0	1	1	1	1	1	1	0	1	1
0	1	1	0	1	1	1	1	1	1	0	1
0	1	1	1	1	1	1	1	1	1	1	0
1	0	0	0	1	1	1	1	1	1	1	1
1	0	0	1	1	1	1	1	1	1	1	1
1	0	1	0	1	1	1	1	1	1	1	1
1	0	1	1	1	1	1	1	1	1	1	1
1	1	0	0	1	1	1	1	1	1	1	1
1	1	0	1	1	1	1	1	1	1	1	1
1	1	1	0	1	1	1	1	1	1	1	1
1	1	1	1	1	1	1	1	1	1	1	1

Figure 9.4   7442 Truth table

demultiplex input data to any one of eight different output lines; the data being transmitted without any inversion. Another way of showing this is given in Figure 9.5.

SELECT INPUTS			OUTPUT CHANNEL AT WHICH DATA APPEARS
C	B	A	NUMBER
0	0	0	0
0	0	1	1
0	1	0	2
0	1	1	3
1	0	0	4
1	0	1	5
1	1	0	6
1	1	1	7

Figure 9.5   Channel selection

Multiplexed memory devices

As mentioned previously, it is of major economic significance to reduce the pin count on an integrated circuit.
With memory devices of ever-growing capacity, a high
pin count can present a problem. Take, for example, a
64 k by 1-bit dynamic RAM. This size of memory *could*
require 16 address lines, but fortunately the number is
reduced by the use of multiplexing. Figure 9.6 shows a
common arrangement used for a 16 k RAM, which might
ordinarily need 14 address lines, but in practice has only
7. The necessary 14 address lines from the host microprocessor are connected to the RAM via two quad 2-input
multiplexers. By the use of only one more signal line,
CAS/$\overline{\text{RAS}}$ (*column address strobe/row address strobe*),
first the top 7 address lines are connected to the RAM,
followed by the next 7 address lines. Internal decoding
within the RAM device along with CAS/$\overline{\text{RAS}}$ enables the

113

Logic design

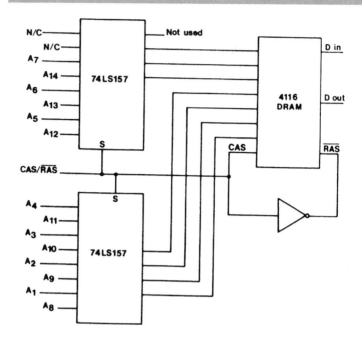

Figure 9.6 *Common arrangement for 16 K RAM*

addressing of the 16 k locations. Of course, this is very diagrammatic, as the refreshing of such a dynamic RAM and how such a strobe signal may be obtained has been completely ignored.

Microprocessor buses

This idea then leads us onto a similar area in which signals intended for different devices share a common route. It is usual in most microprocessor-based equipment for it to communicate with more than one single device; for example, the information from several different memory devices. The signal path along which this information flows is called the *data bus*. In order to speed up the flow of data, and hence the speed of operation of the machine as a whole, the trend has been toward parallel buses and the 8-bit data bus is still the most common. The means whereby the microprocessor selects which device shall have access to the bus, either to accept or transmit data, makes use of the tri-state type of output, which we have encountered previously.

Take note — Take note — Take note — Take note

A typical microprocessor will have three parallel buses; one is the data bus, just mentioned, the second is the *address bus* and the third the *control bus*. These last two buses are used together to determine precisely which device is to be accessed by the microprocessor and whether data is to flow along the data bus in one direction or the other.

Figure 9.7 shows a highly simplified block diagram of such a system in order to illustrate these points. This *system* has a 4-bit address bus, a 4-bit data bus and a 1-bit control bus. Of course, this is much simpler than any *real* system, but more of those in due course. With a 4-bit address bus only 16 memory locations could be

Logic design

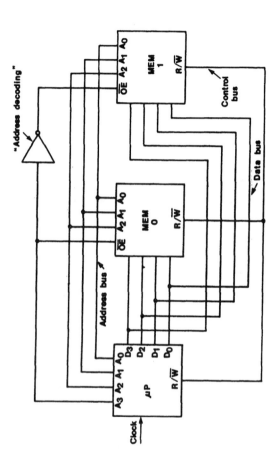

Figure 9.7 Simplified microprocessor

116

addressed and to make our scheme even more artificial, these have been located in two separate devices. Also, with a 4-bit data bus, only 16 unique *words* could be encoded which means our simple microprocessor would have a basic instruction set of 16 operations. This is another reason why its tasks would be limited, although there are ways round the problem. Finally, the control bus has been restricted to a single read/write line, such that if this line is high, data is flowing into the processor and when low, out from it.

With such a simple system only a minimal amount of extra hardware is needed for address decoding. This performs the function of selecting the appropriate device by acting on the address presented on the address bus and producing a single signal which is connected to the output enable pin of the memory device which is used to enable its tri-state outputs. The read/write line of our simple control bus then sets the direction in which data is to flow.

The operation of such a system would be such that when the microprocessor wishes to read a data *word* from memory, it sets the appropriate address on the address bus and the read/write line high. The data presented by the selected location would then flow along the data bus into the processor for it to act upon. This process might be repeated, or for a write to memory, the address is again set, the read/write line goes low and data flows from the microprocessor to modify the contents of a memory location. With such a simple *address decoder* as this (one inverter!), one memory device would be connected to the data bus at all times. However, as the purpose is to prevent more than one peripheral device having access to the bus at any one time, this would not be a problem.

In the next chapter, we shall examine the action of more realistic microprocessor-based systems.

10 Microprocessor-based systems

A possible microprocessor-based system is shown in the circuit of Figure 10.1. This is a Z80-based CPU module design which, although simple and unlikely to be used in many applications, does give an overall understanding of what happens in *any* microprocessor-based system.

First, it is useful to look at the similarities between the design of Figure 10.1 and the crude model of a system shown in Figure 10.2. At first sight, the two may seem completely unrelated, but there are some important similarities which can be pointed out. Both have such features as a data bus, address bus and control bus. For

Logic design

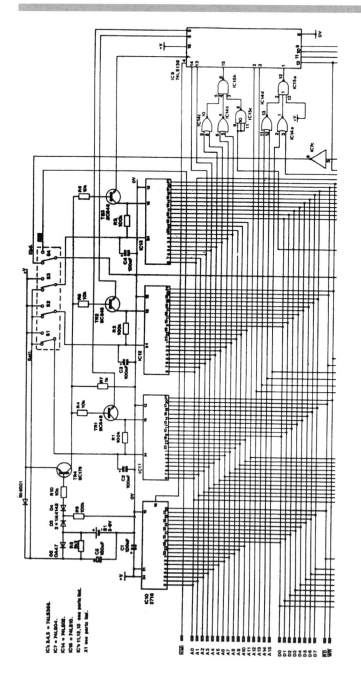

Figure 10.1(a)

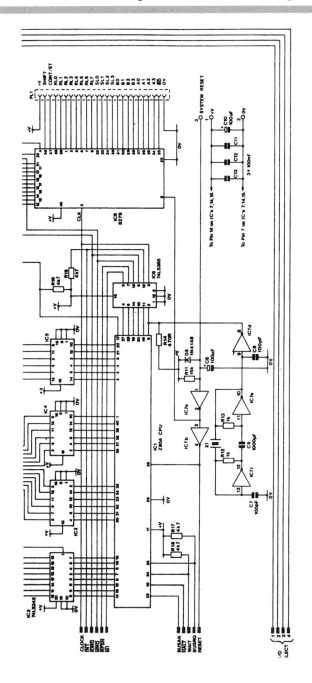

Figure 10.1(b) Maplin Z80 CPU circuit

Logic design

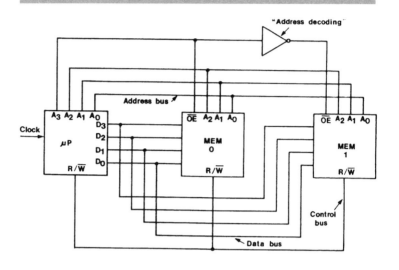

Figure 10.2 Simplified microprocessor

the Z80 the data bus is 8 bits wide and the address bus 16 bits wide. The Z80 control bus consists essentially of four lines, $\overline{\text{MEMREQ}}$, $\overline{\text{I/OREQ}}$, $\overline{\text{READ}}$ and $\overline{\text{WRITE}}$, rather than just a single READ/WRITE line used in the model. There are other signals used by the processor for control purposes, such as BUSAK and M1, but we shall leave these alone for the time being. The main purpose of each of these is as follows:

● $\overline{\text{MEMREQ}}$— this is an active low signal, as indeed are the others in this group, which is asserted to indicate that the address bus contains a valid address,

● $\overline{\text{I/OREQ}}$ — a feature of the Z80 is that it has a separate I/O space, apart from the main 64 K of memory. It is

122

the intention for this to be used to contain all the peripheral devices with which the processor needs to communicate. This line is asserted low to indicate that the bottom eight address lines contain a valid address for an I/O port.,

● $\overline{\text{READ}}$ — this is asserted low to indicate that the processor is able to accept data from a memory location or input device,

● $\overline{\text{WRITE}}$ — similar to read, this is used to indicate that the data bus contains valid data for sending to a selected device.

In some so-called minimum systems, the I/O line may be left unused, but since it is a feature of the Z80 it seems worthy of further explanation.

Memory maps

We have seen memory maps in previous chapters. These are notional maps and simply represent the total amount of memory and I/O space which the processor is capable of addressing. In any real system physical memory, or I/O ports, may only occupy a portion of the total available. The particular feature of the Z80, not shared by other 8-bit devices such as the 6502, is the existence of this separate I/O space. This could be shown as a smaller map alongside the main memory map. The usual function of this space is to act as 256 individual *ports*. That is, addressable locations to which peripheral devices

Logic design

may be connected to the buses via suitable hardware, like latches or buffers. Of course, such devices could be contained within the main memory map when they are referred to as being memory mapped I/O devices. This is unavoidable with some processors, but with the Z80, they can all be put neatly in their own I/O space, leaving the 64 K of main memory uncluttered. This produces the minor problem of how to distinguish between the first 256 bytes of memory and the I/O ports, as they both share a common address bus. This, of course, is achieved by the inclusion of the $\overline{I/OREQ}$ line in the address decoding. Thus:

● to READ from memory location 100D, then the address bus would contain 0064H (= 100D), the $\overline{READ}$ line low and $\overline{MEMREQ}$ low, but with $\overline{I/OREQ}$ high,

● to READ from port 100D, then again the address bus will contain 0064H, $\overline{READ}$ line low, but this time with $\overline{I/OREQ}$ low and $\overline{MEMREQ}$ remaining high.

Stored program

We can now look at the operation of the micro-processor-based module, and explain the significance of some of the other signal lines present. Perhaps at this stage, it is worth reminding the novices there really is nothing magical about a microprocessor! A Z80, a fairly simple device by present day standards, could be made up from discrete logic gates, along the lines that we have been looking at over the past chapters. It would, however, be

124

a rather pointless exercise, as it is the great advantage of VLSI technology that has allowed such circuitry to be *compressed* onto a single chip. But it *can* be done!

The main function of the microprocessor is to work through a set of instructions, the *program*, rather like someone following a recipe in a cookbook.

Take note — Take note — Take note — Take note

The program consists of specific instructions which the microprocessor understands, and it resides in memory. Without such a program, the hardware can do precisely nothing, no matter how sophisticated it may be.

This leads us to something of a paradox, for with any home computer one would expect to enter the program from the keyboard or perhaps a cassette or disk unit. However, the machine must already contain an operational program in order to make any sense of such attempts at data entry.

Such a program, often referred to as the *operating system*, would need to reside in a ROM or on a hard disk as part of the whole machine, ready to spring into action as soon as the power is turned on. The module under discussion has space for both ROM and RAM, but as yet, no

Logic design

program to act as an operating system. The idea here then, would be to write some suitable controlling software on another machine, transfer this when debugged into an EPROM, and plug this into the target system. Likewise, in order for the module to do anything useful, there is still a need for some means of communicating with it, and also, some way in which it can deliver the results of its working.

A microprocessor module such as that in Figure 10.1 can be fitted with a special type of peripheral device, such as the Intel 8279. This has the ability to be interfaced with a simple keyboard for data entry and a 7-segment LED display for data output. This would, though, require a controlling routine as part of the operating system to allow suitable data to be entered into RAM, or to modify the contents of RAM in order for further programs to be written and executed. This would then make it possible for the module to act as, say, a microprocessor-based controller for such applications as regulating the central heating, stage lighting, simple machinery or such-like. This *chicken-and-egg* problem can really only be resolved by access to other programming equipment; one such piece of equipment is the so-called *microprocessor development system*, or simply MDS. These are not really within the scope of the home computer enthusiast, as they often cost several thousand pounds! However, this *would* enable the requisite software to be written and debugged very quickly for the intended task of the module. The way this is achieved is to replace the microprocessor in the module, or the *target* system, with a special plug connecting to the *host*. By this means the operation of all aspects of the target system can be controlled, or emulated, by the host machine. This would

126

also contain sufficient memory for software to be written and debugged using sophisticated programming aids, and then allow the program to be run in the target system, but with the host keeping full control of its execution. With such a tool at one's disposal, complex programs can be produced relatively quickly, and the performance of the target monitored at all times. As a final stage, the finished program can be *burned* into an EPROM, then transferred to the target so it can operate as a stand-alone system.

Another slightly more simple method is to do a similar thing with the ROM resident in the target system, this then allows the program to be written and stored in RAM in a machine often called a *romulator*. The target system has access to this RAM, which *looks* like the operating system which would normally be in ROM. The romulator has the ability to modify the RAM contents, and hence its effect on the operation of the target can be observed. The control of the target is by no means as total as with the MDS, but this is reflected in the lower cost of such a system.

First base — last base

This short discussion on the principles of microprocessor operation brings to an end this book.

During its course, we have looked at some of the aspects of digital electronics, and have of necessity left out a lot more. Hopefully, it may have stimulated some into

Logic design

enquiring further into this fascinating subject, and may have encouraged you to have a go at some construction or experimentation. If you have followed the book this far, then the whole world of the microprocessor lies stretched out before you, with all manner of delights in store! From now on, though, the rest is up to you.

MAPLIN Books